Whispers of the Americas

Tales *of* Travel, Food *and* Culture Across Two Continents

RICHARD H. ROGERS

This book is dedicated to my dear children and grandchildren.
And to the memory of my beloved oldest brother.

TABLE OF CONTENTS

Braised veal shank slow-cooked in a savory broth
with tomatoes, red wine, and garlic until the meat
falls off the bone. It was served with creamy polenta
and a gremolata made from lemon zest, garlic, and
parsley. Simply amazing!

All these dishes combine authentic Latin American
flavors, each with a rich culinary heritage and
unique spices and ingredients native to its region.

INTRODUCTION

Welcome to *Whispers of the Americas*

This is the fourth installment in a five-part series exploring the art of culinary travel—a must-have collection for food and culture enthusiasts Each book serves as a vibrant exploration of the rich intersection between gastronomy, travel, and local culture, guiding readers through the bustling streets of Paris, Beijing, the colorful markets of Istanbul, and the culinary hotspots of Lima, Panama, São Paulo, and beyond. These volumes offer a heartfelt narrative of my journeys, blending evocative storytelling with the unforgettable flavors and experiences I've encountered.

These stories go beyond mere destinations—they capture the essence of the people, the moments of connection, and the bonds forged along the way. Every location showcases a distinct cuisine pivotal in the adventure while emphasizing food and travel's transformative power. Through this lens, I aim to highlight the shared beauty that unites people across the globe.

From one corner of the globe to another, I invite you to savor these tales that celebrate discovery and connection. Through humor, insight, and the memory of remarkable meals in restaurants and family meals while growing up in France, I hope to offer more than just adventures—I share a part of myself and a deeper understanding of the places and people I've encountered.

If the vibrant Latin flavors in my current book leave you wanting more, I encourage you to explore my other volumes. They traverse the charming Left Bank of Paris, the beauty of the Brittany countryside, the sun-drenched landscapes of the South of France, the cobblestone streets of Belgium, the vibrant energy of China, and the beautiful vineyards and scenery of Cape Town, South Africa, among many others. Each journey is deeply personal, yet the themes of discovery, culture, and connection are universal.

Whispers of the Americas is a culinary odyssey along well-traveled roads, offering readers a taste of diverse cultures, stories, and flavors. The book is thoughtfully divided into two sections, each offering a unique glimpse into the worlds I've explored.

Part I is a collection of short stories, primarily fiction, set against the backdrop of iconic U.S. cities. Each story offers a glimpse into a unique facet of American life along with recipes, from the bustling holiday streets of Chicago to the serene Eastern shore of Maryland and from the historic heart of Philadelphia in a time gone by to the vibrant spirit of New Orleans. Among these narratives is a legal case of note—an actual "dog bites dog" story that takes an unexpected twist in court. It's a tale I believe you'll find both amusing and perhaps even thought-provoking.

Part II takes us on a journey through Latin America, a region that has always captivated me. My travels across various countries have deepened my appreciation for the rich cultural diversity and offered insights into the people, their language, and their food. From the historic charm and vibrancy of Mexico City to the culinary brilliance of Lima and Sao Paulo, each destination brings its distinctive fusion of culture and cuisine. I aim to offer a deeper understanding of Latin America's vibrant heritage through these adventures. Each story in this section is accompanied by a thoughtfully curated recipe, perfectly paired with exceptional wines to elevate your culinary journey.

This is at the heart of my belief: great food, unforgettable wine, and captivating stories form an inseparable trinity. With this in mind, I present a collection of irresistibly delicious classic recipes, inviting you to make them your own by being generous with ingredients—after all, cooking is about personal taste and sharing with friends. And yes, I highly recommend a glass of wine while cooking—it's the perfect companion.

Thank you. I hope you enjoy this book as much as I have had the pleasure of putting it all together.

Part I

UNITED STATES

An Autumn Row

Preface to An Autumn Row

I treasure the memories from my years of competitive collegiate and club rowing. It often feels like just yesterday I was out on the water with my teammates, though time has a way of reminding me how far those days are behind me. Seeing a crew team gliding across the water in an eight-oared shell at home or abroad brings back memories of camaraderie, races won and lost, and the pursuit of excellence that defined our days on the water. As a collegiate oarsman and a master's rower, I have had the honor of competing against many formidable crews. Whether on the Schuylkill River in Philadelphia, the Potomac in Washington, DC, the East Harlem, New York City, the Hudson in Upper New York State, or elsewhere, each venue brought its blend of challenges and anticipation. I will forever cherish those experiences.

I can vividly recall those tense, anxious pre-race moments. Each race began with a palpable sense of anticipation and familiar stomach-churning moments as we lined up, crews in sleek racing shells side by side, poised and spring-loaded, ready at the start line. We nervously awaited the commands from the official starter, amplified through a megaphone: First, it was "Coxswains, raise your hands if you are ready." Then came the pivotal moment, "Rowers, sit ready. Ready all. Row!" With the echo of the starting gun, what seemed like chaos transformed into synchronized motion within milliseconds as every rower's oar sliced through the water in practice, precision unison.

Coxswains would scream commands to their crews: "Quarter slide, half slide, full slide, stroke going up on two!" Those early moments were intense, a symphony of controlled frenzy, savagely pitting crew against crew; skill, speed, and endurance were the hallmarks. Each coxswain would bellow out strategic commands to raise the rowing stroke for a quick "power ten," then down again, all to gain an edge or outmaneuver the nearest opposing crew team. And so, it continued for 2000 grueling meters, each one feeling like an eternity, until at last, we heard the sound of the race gun as we crossed the finish line, our bodies drained of every ounce of energy, utterly exhausted.

As my train gradually slowed, approaching Philadelphia's 30th Street Station, my gaze inevitably went toward the serene

Schuylkill River. Perhaps, amidst the tranquil scenery, I would be lucky to spot a crew team diligently practicing their rowing. There, against the backdrop of the city skyline, was the famous Boathouse Row. Without fail, this sight evoked a stirring within me. Its timeless charm makes Philadelphia a poignant repository of countless memories, especially those intertwined with family history.

In bow four, the author practiced on the Chester during
a late fall afternoon more than a few years ago.

An Autumn Row

It was one of those typical late September mornings, damp, chilly, and still dark outside with only the slightest hint of color in the sky as if Mother Nature had somehow come along with brush-stroked pink and yellow hues against her canvas sky. Though dark outside, one discerned silhouettes entering the boathouse and letting an arc of light briefly sweep the early morning darkness each time, revealing a peaceful creek, a wooden dock with steps leading to a second but floating dock where a coach's launch waited patiently. Moments later, the boathouse came alive as the metal doors rattled up and out of sight, and the bow of an elegant 65 ft or just under twenty meters long, narrow racing shell jutted out. It was carried delicately yet with resolute firmness on the shoulders of eight oarsmen in various attire, some wearing shorts in defiance of the cold weather, others in full sweat gear, some with racing gloves, and others with wool caps most surely pushed on their heads by a concerned loved one.

When her stern cleared the boathouse, the crew silently marched her to the floating dock. The little coxswain, wrapped in sweatpants, hat, and gloves and looking quite like a child about to play in the snow, let out a series of quick, sharp commands that raised the elegant lady high over the heads of the rowers, and then fluidly she was brought down to waist level and placed, ever so gently, in the dark still waters of the creek, for one last time. There was still only the promise of the morning sun as the crew silently pushed off from the dock. Listening carefully, one could make out the lady slowly coming to life, the creaking of her wooden slides, the splash of an oar, a muffled command from the stern, the tapping of the cadence on her gunwales, and then she and her crew disappeared into the morning mist towards the river.

She was always elegant and very much the Grande Dame of the boathouse. Her original home was Olympia, Washington. However, she had traveled and competed in some of the great East Coast rowing classics, with Philadelphia and Boston among her favorite venues. Since those heady days of competition, so much had changed for her; she felt out of place, considered almost a relic compared to the young international upstarts making her house their home. In a way, she envied them; how could she not? They had state-of-the-art technology with strange and mysterious words like hyper-carbon, woven carbon fibers, and T-6 aluminum. It was as if they were speaking another language. Nevertheless, she wore her cuts and scrapes like a real badge of honor. It made her remember more than one well-meaning young man hitting her gunwales or cracking her hull in more than one place.

After all these years, epoxy could well have been her middle name. She was fitted with handsome rigging, brass fittings, and oarlocks, which held her eight elegant 12-foot (3.6 meters) sweep oars. They were majestic-looking oars that seemed to reach the sky and were beautifully varnished, with the blades painted a deep red with two horizontal, broad white stripes. In her time, she had seen so many rowers come and go that it was hard to remember one from another. She sensed some already knew what they were doing and how best to work with her; they were confident but also careful and gentle, learning how to get her effortlessly gliding across the blue waters. Other rowers started each season with two left feet, seemingly determined to work against her rather than with her. But season after season, her boys eventually learned the art of finesse rowing as a team and propelled her across many a cheering finish line. That made her genuinely happy.

When all eight of her boys and her little coxswain finally settled in, she carried an accumulated weight of close to 1500 pounds (or 680 Kg). To be sure, she had handled more weight in her time, especially in choppy waters or with inexperienced crews when she would take on water that would rush from bow to stern, finally settling in her engine room. All that was fine with her; she was forgiving, and somehow, instinctively, she made the proper adjustments. But above all else, flat water and an experienced crew brought her to life and ignited her engines. Her engines would genuinely hum when all eight of her boys rowed in perfect harmony, moving in unison, perfectly repeating each stroke, time and time, with all eight blades slicing through the water. One could hear the gurgle of water beneath her hull as she jumped forward with each massive new stroke displacing the water, leaving only eight puddles behind her bow. As the saying goes: "When eight row together with swing, the boat becomes the ninth rower."

It was full daylight as the crew headed back to the boathouse. She was happy, confident that her boys, all eight soaking wet, tired, and happy, had enjoyed the morning row.

It was a good workout. They knew it, and she knew it. They worked well together. But this was her last time. She was hoisted gallantly up from the water and steered to a spot where a pair of wooden horses awaited just outside the boathouse along the side wall where she would wait, maybe forever, for her boys to return. A group of eight girls confidently and proudly walked by dressed in multi-colored fashionable rowing gear and carrying a new fiberglass shell with a bright yellow hull. "Up to your shoulders," the little coxswain loudly snapped her command as they neared the water.

The story is dedicated to my father, an oarsman himself, but many years ago, while a student at a prep school in New Hampshire.

THE HOUSE ACROSS THE CREEK

The Chesapeake Bay, the largest estuary in the United States, takes its name from the Algonquian Indian word meaning "village at a big river." This majestic bay has long been central to the region's economic and political landscape, spanning over 200 miles and cradling numerous tributaries like the Choptank, Nanticoke, Pocomoke, and Patuxent rivers. Yet, as time has passed, the challenge of preserving this fragile ecosystem has grown, with the relentless push for progress exacting a toll on its delicate balance.

Though far more modest in scale than the grand Chesapeake, this story—a brief moment frozen in time—finds itself intimately tied to the bay's legacy. Along Maryland's Eastern Shore, a pictur-esque haven lies a stone's throw from a peaceful creek winding its way into a tributary and eventually merging with the Chesapeake. Here, despite the march of time, the landscape remains largely unspoiled, a serene escape seemingly untouched by the rush of modern life.

Jack Dearborn, with Washington, D.C. safely in his rear-view mirror, was relieved to be off the crowded Route 50 and now barreling down back roads as flat as a griddle and straight as an arrow, with endless rows of soybean and cornfields stretch-ing out on either side. The towering corn stalks, lush and green, nearly kissed the sky, destined, Jack knew, for the large poultry plants near Salisbury. An hour after crossing the Bay Bridge, Jack carefully steered his classic British Racing Green 1965 MGB GT through the narrow, almost hidden entrance, the tires softly crunching over a gravel driveway once paved with oyster shells.

He parked in front of "Belle View," a graceful, white-framed, black-shuttered Tidewater "telescope" house—so called for its ar-chitectural style, in which the structure appears to collapse like a telescope due to the series of smaller units, each progressively lower than the last. Built in the late 1600s by a wealthy mer-chant, Belle View had been home to generations of his descen-dants, standing witness to the Revolutionary War, the Civil War, the Great Depression, two world wars, and the ebb and flow of family fortunes. Now a registered national historic landmark, the house still carried the echoes of history within its walls.

As the late afternoon sun bore down mercilessly, the heat radiated from the ground, and the air seemed to hang heavy with the infamous August humidity of the Eastern Shore. Jack felt it cling to him like a damp, suffocating blanket. Stepping out of the car, he was greeted by a familiar symphony of scents—the sharp tang of freshly cut grass, the earthy musk from the nearby creek, the resinous aroma of pine, faint wisps of charcoal smoke drifting from a distant grill, and a fresh hint of paint from some unseen project. Together, these elements blended into an intoxicating bouquet that filled the air, imbuing the place with a distinct, almost nostalgic charm.

The quiet was suddenly interrupted by the low hum of an inboard engine. Jack turned just in time to catch sight of a sleek sailboat rounding the bend. With a laid-back confidence, the skipper deftly motored her up the creek toward the deeper, open waters of the Chesapeake Bay. He wore aviator sunglasses and a red baseball cap, giving Jack a casual nod and a quick smile before turning his attention back to the helm. Two children perched excitedly near the bow, barely containing their eagerness for the evening sail, while a sun-kissed, long-legged woman managed the lines with the same easy competence as the skipper. At the entrance to the cabin, a golden retriever lounged contentedly as if guarding the heart of the floating home.

Jack watched the boat slowly vanish into the distance. Across the creek from Belle View, a stately Georgian home stood on a piece of land that jutted into the water. Its perfectly manicured lawns gently sloped down to the water's edge, a sight that never failed to catch his eye. Jack had long been intrigued by the house across the creek, though he knew little about its owners—only that they were a couple from New York City. Originally summer residents, they had since traded their Park Avenue apartment for a permanent life on the Eastern Shore. Jack could easily understand why.

The house was nothing short of spectacular. It boasted panoramic views of the creek, the river, and the distant horizon. Large windows and French doors spanned the entire façade, offering sweeping views from any room inside. The owners had even constructed a grand staircase that descended to a private dock, where a sleek 48-foot sloop rested, ready for adventure.

From his spot across the creek, Jack never tired of admiring the grandeur of the home, the dock, and the ever-changing landscape beyond.

Jack grabbed his bag from the car and headed back to where the neatly manicured lawn met a flagstone walkway, which curved toward a small picket fence enclosing a large kidney-shaped pool. Flanking either end of the pool were tables with umbrellas, easy chairs, and an assortment of inflatable floats. As expected, Billie was lounging at one end, dressed in what could barely be called a swimsuit, topped with an oversized wide-brimmed straw hat. Her favorite drink, a Maker's Mark Old Fashioned, was sweating on a coaster beside her, while a cigarette, held in a long black vintage sequin holder, smoldered lazily between her fingers.

Peeking over her stylish sunglasses, she started with a pout but then smiled and said, "Jack, darling, it's unbearably hot, and why are you still standing there? Go put on your trunks. You know where the towels are by now."

He grinned. "Thanks, Billie. You're swell; I think I can manage all of that quite easily," he said, turning towards the house. She called after him, "And darling, fix yourself something real cold. The bar's been open for hours, and I was hoping you would come and entertain me. I've been so lonely all day with no one to talk to."

Billie often seemed to inhabit a world of her own, as if suspended in a different era. Once, with a wistful smile, she confided in him, "If I could step into a time capsule, I'd whisk myself straight back to the roaring 1920s, never to return. Paris, of course, would be my sanctuary." Her insistence on this detail was unmistakable. The 1920s had an undeniable pull on Billie—the lively music, the glamorous fashion, the indulgent lifestyle. Yet, at times, her fascination veered into obsession, especially after a few Old Fashioneds. She'd passionately insist that an ancestor had somehow possessed her body, mind, and soul. "You know it's possible, don't you, Jack? Please, tell me you do." These conversations were always challenging, especially when Bourbon blurred the lines between fantasy and reality.

After the passing of her parents and eventually her beloved brother, whom she "simply adored," Billie lived alone on the family estate. Her only constant companion was "darling Kikka," a Cocker Spaniel, oddly more neurotic than Billie herself. Three days a week, the housekeeper, Bertina—Bertie to those who knew her—would stop by to check on Billie, ensuring she had groceries or any special requests from the town's lone greengrocer. She'd also tidy up as needed. Bertie's son, Amos, who Billie claimed had a habit of taking his time mowing the lawn, especially when she happened to be sunbathing by the pool, would also handle the leaves and hedge trimming in the fall. In winter, Amos would attempt to shovel the driveway, provided his car could navigate the long, snow-buried back road—one the county snowplows had never once touched.

Jack recalled that Billie may have been living alone, but there had been talk—whether he'd been told directly or pieced it together himself—that a string of suitors had tried their luck with her. Each one, it was said, had claimed to outdo the last in winning her favor. This was the usual chatter among certain trust fund boys, who spent their afternoons lounging at the Golf or Yacht Club bars, drinking in mass quantities and speculating about which of the latest girls in town might be "available." At the same time, they idly planned for the upcoming goose season. Even if someone had briefly won Billie's attention, none had managed to stick around. Billie had dismissed them as "boring, dull, and not at all peppy," adding with a sly smile, "Not like you, Jack." He'd chew on that comment while waiting for the other shoe to drop.

Sure, Billie was appealing in more ways than one, even a little wild at times. They made each other laugh, and she could cook up a storm when she wanted. Jack had skirted the line with her but never quite crossed it. Sometimes, he thought about throwing caution to the wind—but for now, he'd play it safe.

Emerging in his plaid swim trunks, Jack carried a monogrammed bath towel slung over one shoulder and a tall gin and tonic with extra limes in his other hand. Without hesitation, he dove into the water, swimming easily beneath the surface until he reached the far side of the pool. He surfaced with a splash, sending a spray that made Billie shriek in surprise.

"You're simply impossible, Jack Dearborn! Now I'm all wet because of you!" Billie shrieked playfully as she dove in after him, resuming their water fight with the glee of two carefree children. The afternoon heat weighed on them, but the cool pool was their sanctuary. They lingered as long as they could, aware that the setting sun would soon summon an aerial assault of insects—dive-bombers the size of small helicopters. You could hear the distant hum of wings, warning of the impending attack. Soon, they'd swarm in formation, hungry for the sweetness of suntan oil-lathered skin.

Reluctantly abandoning the poolside, they retreated to the deck, where the creek spread out like glass before them. While still in their swimsuits, they indulged in a candlelit feast that Jack had masterfully prepared. Thick, rare T-bone steaks sizzled on the grill, accompanied by sweet Eastern Shore corn on the cob, dripping with butter and sprinkled generously with salt and pepper. Juicy slices of beefsteak tomatoes gleamed with a dash of mayonnaise and seasonings, while a fresh green salad glistened in a light vinegar and oil dressing. The meal was perfectly complemented by a chilled, crisp Sauvignon Blanc from New Zealand and, for contrast, a bold Chianti Classico. Dessert was Billie's masterpiece— chewy brownies crowned with scoops of vanilla ice cream, a fitting finale to their quintessential summer feast.

As the last rays of the sun disappeared, leaving a streak of deep red across the horizon, they waited in the growing dusk. Then, as if on cue, the night sky exploded into a dazzling display of multicolored fireworks, each burst painting the heavens before tumbling down into the inky waters below. Across the creek, their neighbors had put on yet another extravagant show, the finest New York had to offer. Through the brilliant flashes, the grand estate on the far shore was illuminated, the French doors revealing glimpses of guests mingling on the lawn. Laughter and applause echoed across the water with every new sunburst overhead.

Jack leaned closer to Billie, his voice soft and amused. "I feel like Nick Carraway watching Gatsby's parties from across the bay," he said, knowing she'd catch the literary reference. Nick, the quiet observer, watching the grand spectacle of wealth and indulgence just beyond his reach.

Billie clapped her hands,

> "Oh, Jack, I simply love that! From now on, I shall call you Nick; you don't mind, do you? I do hope not." Jack smiled and assured Billie it was fine, "but only in private—others wouldn't understand."

Together, they savored the final moments of the fireworks. Across the creek, the house shimmered in the afterglow, pulsating with the rhythm of the celebration: the clink of glasses, the lilting strains of music, and bursts of infectious laughter. Each brilliant explosion of color drew ripples of applause from the gathering, echoing with each crescendo in the sky, where vibrant hues danced over the still waters below. Then, as suddenly as it had begun, the display ended, leaving behind a deep, hushed stillness.

Jack lingered outside, finishing his cigar, lost in the fading beauty of the moment. From inside the house, he could hear faint notes of music—Bessie Smith's voice drifting through the air, singing *Downhearted Blues*. "Gee, but it's hard to love someone when that someone don't love you." Billie was getting herself worked up again. "Nick," she cried once, then again, louder. "Nick, are you ever planning on coming inside?"

"If it wasn't for the mist, we could see your home across the bay....You always have a green light that burns all night at the end of your dock."
(F.S. Fitzgerald, The Great Gatsby)

SHRIMP, GRITS AND ABSINTHE IN THE FRENCH QUARTER

I arrived in the Big Easy, ready to immerse myself in the rich French heritage that courses through the veins of the city. Yet, my visit seemed to hold more complexity than I first imagined. The French Quarter (*Le Quartier Français*), the iconic heart of New Orleans, embodied every tale I'd heard—both its vibrant charm and the cautionary whispers. From its undeniable charm to its edgier side, the advice was always the same: "Never wander alone, stick to groups of three or more, keep your wallet anywhere but your back pocket," and my favorite, "Make sure you've got a doctor on speed dial—just in case!"

For all the tales I'd heard about New Orleans, this place defined the term "Hot LZ." It was an enticing blend of chaos and allure. Having lived in central Africa, navigated the gritty docks and alleys of Antwerp, handled myself in the rowdy beer houses of Brussels, and explored the far reaches of Beijing, Saigon, Istanbul, and beyond, I was far from fazed. I ventured into the damp streets of the Quarter on a dreary day, where the drizzle only intensified the heavy humidity that clung to me like a wet blanket. Driven by an unrelenting thirst, I pressed on through the sultry haze.

Who Invited the Green Fairy?

I found myself at the Absinthe House, tucked unassumingly on the corner of Bienville and Bourbon Street. No grand entrance marked this hidden gem—just a dimly lit, unpretentious hole in the wall. Inside, a U-shaped bar cradled a few scattered patrons. Some, lost in their drinks, stared vacantly into space, perhaps reliving memories of what might have been. Time slips away. The bartender handed me a weathered, plastic-covered menu with well-worn pages detailing everything one might want about absinthe and a collection of pricey, daring concoctions for the bold-hearted.

Determined to do some on-site research, I opted to pace myself through a series of absinthe tastings. The pale green liquor, steeped in myth and mystery, has been blamed for all manner of sins, from foolish drunken antics to outright murder.

Anise flavor comes from a carefully guarded blend of herbs, including fennel and wormwood—a bitter plant famous for its supposed health benefits and infamous for its rumored hallucinogenic properties. In large doses, wormwood has been blamed for everything from convulsions to psychosis, seizures, and even dangerous behavior, which, over time, has woven absinthe into a cloak of mystery and fear. This lore has fueled its dark allure, associating it with madness and murder among those daring enough to indulge.

But there's more to absinthe than its reputation. In the Absinthe House, the experience transcends simply pouring a drink. The ritual follows the traditional Parisian absinthe drip: a sugar cube is placed on a slotted spoon above a glass of absinthe, and then cold water is slowly poured over the cube, allowing it to dissolve into the liquor. This ritual initiates the "louching" process, where the spirit thickens and turns cloudy as the water draws out the herbal essences. "Adding sugar and water to absinthe highlights its botanical sweetness while making the high-proof spirit easier to sip." Just how high-proof are we talking? Historically, absinthe has ranged from 100 to 150 proof (50–75% alcohol by volume), but some varieties reach up to 179 proof (89% ABV). The high alcohol content helps preserve its iconic green color, also known as *la fée verte*—the green fairy.

And if you ever find yourself drifting through surreal, mind-bending realms, you can thank the mischievous green fairy. In my fraternity (best forgotten) days, we didn't have absinthe—our closest equivalent was grain alcohol. Known for its absurdly high proof and notoriety at frat parties, it was infamous for its ability to fuel wild nights and rumors of potential blindness from prolonged usage. We'd make late-night runs to that sketchy liquor store across the river, the one meant for locals, not for overconfident, cocky college kids like us.

With its deep ties to bohemian culture, Absinthe unsurprisingly became a target for social conservatives and prohibitionists, who saw it as a symbol of indecency and moral decay. The drink garnered a notorious reputation, with famous figures such as Charles Baudelaire, Paul Verlaine, Arthur Rimbaud, Henri de Toulouse-Lautrec, Amedeo Modigliani, Vincent van Gogh, Oscar Wilde, Aleister Crowley, and Alfred Jarry becoming linked to its allure. These so-called 'bad men' of their time were either devotees of, or rumored to be under the influence of, the Green Fairy. One could almost envision society's gradual disintegration, with the only soft laughter echoing from the Green Fairy herself—a truth we both know too well.

But let's leave that behind and return to Bourbon Street, to my days at the Absinthe House...

As my tastings progressed, I continually brushed off a mischievous little green fairy who seemed intent on perching on my shoulder. She whispered persuasively, urging me to abandon reason in favor of indulgence. "Yes, another—and yet another!" she insisted. "*Allez*, be off with you!" I finally cried, shooing her away. She fluttered off with a visible pout, though I knew she'd return, eager to charm the next soul who was just a bit too curious for their own good.

It wasn't until 1912 that the real absinthe was banned, and for good reason. It had already laid waste to a generation of innocently curious drinkers. The psychoactive allure of absinthe was condemned for its toxic effects, often leading to madness. A generation of artists, poets, musicians, and painters lamented its absence, and I can almost feel their pain.

To change course slightly, I was hardly surprised to learn that America's first cocktail, the Sazerac, was invented in New Orleans.

A bartender with hollowed eyes and a complexion that suggested he was more dead than alive gave me a quick history of the drink as he mixed bourbon, herbs, and bitters, finishing it off with a lemon peel. I raised my glass to toast the Big Easy, but truth be told, the drink left much to be desired. It was an acquired taste, perhaps, or maybe someone's odd preference for mouthwash. It reminded me of a cocktail I had in Hanoi, supposedly a favorite of novelist Graham Greene. That one, at least, became much more palatable after the third round.

As I wandered down Bourbon Street, dipping in and out of bars and venues, I soaked in the vibrant music scene—snippets of jazz, blues, and rock mingling with the night air. I passed on the frozen Hurricanes, the signature drink of New Orleans. Tempting, sure, but my Mardi Gras history with that concoction is best left untold. Let's say we're not on good terms. But Bourbon Street? It offers a little bit of everything, a sensory buffet where all tastes are catered to for a price. You can take what you want—just be ready to pay for it, one way or another. The real cost, as always, hits the next day.

Eventually, I returned to my hotel in the French Quarter, just far enough from the Bourbon Street chaos to enjoy some peace. A light fog had settled, and the streets were eerily silent. Now and then, I thought I heard footsteps, the faint clatter of boots, and the unmistakable rattle of a saber in its sheath. My hotel had its charm—a rustic, old-world vibe steeped in history. And, this being New Orleans, naturally, it came with its own ghost stories. The building was owned by a French family who had fled France; tragically, the mother and her young son were murdered, though no one knows by whom. Like all haunted places, the stories swirl about encounters with unsettled spirits, said to have startled more than one unsuspecting guest.

After a quick nightcap in the hotel bar, I declined an invitation to a rooftop party and headed to my room. Haunted tales are good, but I wasn't expecting flying frying pans or beds levitating at night. Still, I double-locked the door, shoved a chair under the handle, bolted the windows facing the balcony, and secured the porch door for good measure. I wasn't too worried.

Food for Thought

As I stand here, let me recommend your next trip to the "Big Easy." If you've ever strolled through New Orleans and enjoyed its vibrant culinary scene, I suggest you stop at Bourbon House. Far be it from me to tell you where to go, but this spot offers a southern dining experience that's hard to beat. You're guaranteed exceptional food and service wherever you sit—at the busy and fun bar or an inviting table draped in a classic checkered cloth.

Should you choose Bourbon House, I urge you to try a dish that will transport your taste buds straight to the bayou. I'm talking about the bourbon, maple shrimp, and grits—a plate so rich in flavor that it deserves to be savored with a glass (or two) of dry French champagne. California bubbles, if you must. There are many versions of this dish, but the one I indulged in during a late-morning meal in the French Quarter was unforgettable. I suspect Jean Lafitte himself would have approved.

I kicked off the feast with a half-dozen charbroiled oysters and a half-dozen Louisiana oysters on the half-shell. Fresh horseradish and Louisiana hot sauce were, of course, mandatory accompaniments. Each bite was heavenly, with the briny oysters serving as the true nectar of the gods. I could've easily ordered another round, but I knew even more greatness would come.

A quick note about the bread basket: it arrives with the rolls all nice and warm, begging for butter to melt over the various homemade selections. You'll shamelessly request a second basket and perhaps even sneak some away for a "sick friend" at home. I'm just saying.

You catch the waiter's eye and inform him that a glass of French champagne would perfectly complement your order of shrimp and grits. He smiles, "An excellent suggestion, sir. I'll return shortly with your champagne and place your order." (A mental note for home: if you ever serve champagne with this dish, make an entrance—draw your saber and dramatically slice off the cork as if you're on the battlefield, fighting the British. Jean Lafitte would surely approve.)

When the dish arrived, it was everything I remembered and more. Sautéed large Gulf shrimp over a bed of creamy homemade grits, accompanied by andouille sausage, mushrooms, and scallions drizzled with a sweet New Orleans-style bourbon glaze. A slice of heaven, right here in the Big Easy.

After loosening my belt, it was time to consider dessert. I glanced at the menu, torn between the crème brûlée, apple pie bread pudding, and bananas foster. Choosing just one felt like an impossible task. I sought the waiter's guidance, but his enthusiasm for every dessert left me no wiser. It was like asking a mechanic if your car needs a tune-up.

At last, I narrowed it down to two: the bread pudding or the bananas foster. With the wisdom of Solomon, I ultimately chose the latter. Bananas sautéed in butter, sugar, and cinnamon, flambéed in rum, and served over vanilla ice cream—what could go wrong? The fiery rum burst might burn off the alcohol, but the flavor remains intoxicating.

What I adore about Bananas Foster is the drama of it all. They are typically prepared tableside, with the flames drawing as much attention as the taste. I half-expected the waiter to laugh at my hesitation, but learning of my choice of dessert, he smiled, "Of course," his tone almost whispering, "Was there ever really any other choice?"

Snow Geese at Spaniard Neck Farm

The morning sky mirrored the biting, deeply penetrating cold that enveloped the land. Locals often warned of more snow on the horizon, and their instincts were rarely wrong. It was early January on the Eastern Shore of Maryland, where the flat, bleak landscape stretched endlessly, offering little more than feed corn and soybean fields as far as the eye could see. The occasional farmhouse punctuated the monotony, often accompanied by one or more grain silos rising like relics of the Cold War, their silhouettes evoking the image of missile launchers on standby.

In this desolate expanse, silence ruled, broken only by the distant rumble of a solitary truck navigating salt-weathered backroads. This was January on the Eastern Shore.

High above, a different world played out. Snow geese swirled in the sky, their movements a chaotic, unchoreographed frenzy, darting and spiraling unpredictably. Their erratic dance starkly contrasted the disciplined formations of their larger cousins, the Canadian geese, who had long since migrated south. Periodically, the snow geese would break from their swirling patterns, descending in a cacophony of honks, their raucous descent disrupting the calm. Below, the fields lay under a frosty, crackling blanket of snow, concealing the remnants of the last corn or soybean harvest.

Suddenly, the stillness of the morning shattered. The sharp crack of gunfire rang out, each shot echoing rapidly across the frozen landscape. Instantly, the geese exploded into a collective panic, their flight ribbons twisting and turning erratically as they shot back into the sky, veering one way and then another in a desperate, disordered escape.

Goose hunting season in these parts has always been a profound and passionate business. This was hunt country. Make no bones about it; goose or deer hunting ranked high as a favorite pastime sport. Football was a close second. At the nearby small liberal arts college, dating back to the 1700s, local students were known to be absent on the opening day of deer or goose hunting. Some things were just understood.

Jeremy Pembroke had roamed these lands since boyhood. The Eastern Shore was in his blood, with good reason: his ancestors had once owned vast tracts of land granted to the Pembroke family by King Charles II in 1650. Over the centuries, the estate was divided, with parcels sold to developers. Yet, a portion remained under cultivation. Jeremy had inherited a sizable stretch of this land, along with the family's stately home, Spaniard Neck Farm, an elegant estate overlooking the serene Chester River, built at the turn of the century.

Maintaining the property consumed Jeremy's time and placed a significant financial burden on him. His ex-wife, a Philadelphia socialite, had never fully grasped his deep connection to the land or his passion for preserving it. Over the years, Jeremy had been tempted more than once to sell the estate. He'd received unsolicited offers from wealthy individuals—primarily hunters and sailors—who appreciated the beauty and uniqueness of this corner of Maryland. Despite the allure of these offers, Jeremy couldn't shake his bond with the land that had defined his family for generations.

Visitors seeking accommodation during peak hunting season often found themselves scrambling for a room, as local hotels were booked far in advance by eager hunting parties. Entering a hotel lobby at dawn, one might momentarily mistake the scene for a military muster. Hunters of all ages, donned in camouflage, filled the space, reflecting the region's deep-rooted hunting tradition—a cherished activity that binds generations.

Jeremy sat in his hunting blind, strategically placed along a hedgerow that bordered a field where his decoys were carefully set. The decoys were positioned downwind from the hedgerow, with the upwind edge of the spread about thirty yards from his blind. He reloaded his Belgian-made Browning A-500 12-gauge semi-automatic shotgun, his eyes scanning the horizon as he awaited the return of his trusted companion, Molson. The 8-year-old Golden Retriever, whom Jeremy had trained since puppyhood, was an exceptional gun dog, always eager to retrieve the prize. For Jeremy, gunning without Molson was unimaginable—the two were inseparable. It wasn't unusual to spot Molson's golden-red head grinning out the passenger window of Jeremy's mud-splattered green Ram 3500 V8 pickup truck. His other vehicle, a silver BMW M5, was a stark contrast—an over-the-top machine designed for high-speed driving, though it spent most of its time tucked away under a tarp in the farm's garage.

With the plump goose retrieved and safely tucked away, Jeremy would field-dress it soon. He blew his zinc goose call, shouldered his Browning, and waited. Late-season geese were always more cautious, adding to the challenge.

The name Spaniard Neck, as legend has it, originated from Spanish explorers who sailed into the Chesapeake Bay in 1526, naming the area Santa Maria. This name appeared on a map as early as 1556. The region's history is rich, once frequented by Spanish, French, and English ships navigating the Chester, Corsica, and Choptank rivers. Stories of pirates and sunken Spanish galleons off the Eastern Shore abound. Spaniard Neck Farm, a tribute to this history, is styled after an 18th-century English country estate. Upon entering, visitors are greeted by a graceful hallway leading past a magnificent circular staircase. To the left, a formal dining room seats ten; to the right, an elegant living room connects to a cozy den. The den, painted in deep green and red, features a glass-encased mahogany gun rack and a fully stocked bar capable of accommodating the most specific requests. Every room, including the upstairs bedrooms, boasts a working fireplace. On the north side of the home, a sunroom invites guests to relax. Outside, brick walkways meander through manicured lawns, gently sloping down to the Chester River. From the pavilion, one can sit and watch merchant ships appear over the horizon, homeward bound from distant lands. It is a place where time stands still; Spaniard Neck Farm offered a peaceful retreat—perhaps a bit too tranquil for some. After a long day of hunting, Jeremy returned with his haul of geese, handing them off to the helpful kitchen staff to be prepared for dinner. His faithful companion, Molson, followed him into the den, where he settled by the fireplace with a contented sigh, though his watchful eyes never left Jeremy. Only when his master sank into a chair, a cocktail in one hand and his other resting gently on Molson's fur, did the dog finally relax, his tail thumping in quiet delight.

MELVIN'S HABERDASHERY

The sign over the front door left no room for confusion:

Melvin's Haberdashery, Established 1921
Clothiers for Gentlemen (and Little Gentlemen, too).

Corporal Leopold Melvin of the 1st Signal Corps, United States Army Expeditionary Force, returned from the First World War physically unscathed—save for a bout of dysentery, recurring trench foot, partial hearing loss, and more nightmares than he cared to admit. In those deep dreams, he was once again Corporal Melvin. The cries of wounded men drifted through the dark, their voices faint yet unmistakable, some calling for their mothers. German artillery shells, packed with mustard gas, screamed overhead while the distant rattle of machine guns echoed. An officer's whistle would pierce the air, followed by the all-too-familiar command: "Over the top, boys!" And always, that same paralyzing fear gripped him, refusing to release its hold. Melvin would jolt awake in these moments, drenched in cold sweat and gasping for breath. He was one of the lucky ones.

Leo Melvin had another dream—a grand and elegant one. He longed to own a haberdashery, inspired by the refined establishments he'd admired on the rue de Rivoli in Paris or the stately streets of London. And so, he pursued this vision with unwavering determination. On a bustling corner of Market and Broad Streets, just as the festive glow of the Christmas season began to shimmer, Leo proudly opened the doors to his shop.

On their way to Wannamaker's department store, curious passersby would pause, pressing their noses against the glass, while a few dared to step inside. There, they found what seemed less a store and more a sanctuary for the sartorially inclined—a shrine to men's fashion. The atmosphere was hushed, almost reverent, as customers engaged in the serious business of outfitting themselves. Speaking in quiet tones, Advisors presented bolts of fine imported worsted wool—light grays, dark blues, conservative stripes, and glen plaids—each fabric unfurled with a ceremony that seemed to honor the cloth and the man who would wear it.

Well-dressed, important-looking gentlemen ran their fingers over the luxurious fabrics, nodding in approval to eager attendants who hovered anxiously nearby. Measurements were taken with care. Collars were matched to shirts and ties—striped, knit, or otherwise discrete. Every detail mattered.

The shop exuded an exclusive men's club atmosphere, where every fitting was performed with ritualistic precision, and clothing was treated with the reverence it deserved. For Leo Melvin, attire was far more than mere decoration—it was identity, a declaration. He often cited with unwavering conviction, "Clothes make the man." From his office, perched above the showroom floor, Leo meticulously observed clients and staff. When a notable customer walked through the doors, he would descend the grand iron spiral staircase, his movements marked by a quiet elegance. His bow, subtle yet deliberate, set the tone. This personal touch, simple as it was, made all the difference. Clients treasured it—and it never failed to pay off.

Leo couldn't have been more pleased. His fabrics were authentic, imported from the finest mills, and though they came with steep price tags, his customers never flinched. Business was booming, and to Leo, it was no surprise—after all, he sold only the best.

Many years later, Benjamin Melvin, the son and successor of Mr. Leopold Melvin, had firmly taken the reins of the family business. The world had changed dramatically: another global war had come and gone, and modern ideas and trends were flooding the marketplace at breakneck speed, particularly from the advertising world of Madison Avenue. Yet Bennie, as he was often called, had an instinct for the business that some believed surpassed even his father's. One of his most astute decisions was the addition of a boys' line with the slogan "and little gentlemen too," cleverly targeting young customers, many of whom were destined for the same prestigious prep schools their fathers had attended. This move ensured that a new generation of young men would be groomed to appreciate fine attire from an early age.

Despite the evolving times, Bennie remained loyal to the core principles that had defined Melvin's Haberdashery under his father's leadership: offering exquisite clothing for gentlemen. The store's offerings ranged from Batiste pajamas and silk drawstring underwear to gentleman's garters and cashmere dressing gowns. It featured the finest French linen shirts, custom-tailored three-button suits, lambswool V-neck sweaters, English hunting vests, colorful Repp and Bow ties, imported wool driving caps, and leather gloves. Even the right aftershaves for a true gentleman were displayed, including the sophisticated "1872 Perfume for Men" by Clive Christian, "Pour Monsieur" by Parfum Caron, and the ever-popular Royall Lyme of Bermuda.

I vividly recall my first day working at Melvin's Haberdashery. A young clerk led me to meet Mr. Benjamin Melvin, or as most called him, ol' man Melvin. He had a tuft of gray hair sprouting from his shiny bald head, and his right eye was a glass one, the result of an accident from long ago. It was difficult to tell whether he was looking directly at you or staring past you, so you quickly learned to address him by focusing on his nose. He was always impeccably dressed, never seen without a perfectly tailored suit, his gold pocket watch neatly tucked into his vest. That pocket watch ruled the rhythm of the store as he used it to open the front doors each morning and close them each evening.

My interview with Mr. Melvin occurred in his office, which had been his father's before him. He sat behind his desk, with a clear view of the sales floor, while I stood nervously before him. He wasted no time and launched into a barrage of questions: Could I distinguish between different types of tweed? Did I know the nuances of imported linen shirts or the difference between Egyptian cotton and Oxford cloth? He quizzed me on formal evening wear, from studs and cummerbunds to the various types of collars. I fumbled through the interview, unsure of most answers, and left the office with my hat in hand, utterly convinced I would never step foot on that sales floor again.

But I was wrong. Over time, I became well-versed in gentleman's attire, and I owe much of that education to ol' man Melvin. He imparted clothing knowledge that has stayed with me even now.

Years later, I returned to the corner of Chestnut and Broad Streets. The haberdashery that had once stood as a pillar of refined fashion was replaced by an expensive steakhouse. It seemed time had moved forward with relentless certainty, and Melvin's Haberdashery had become just another casualty of change.

Portrait of a Town That Time Forgot

*C*aution Readers: If y'all are fans of grits and red eye gravy, cornbread, hush puppies, and sweet tea all served up with a healthy dose of Americana, southern-style that is, like Piggly-Wiggly's and Brew-Thru's, Beach Music and shagging, Blockade Runners (historical-kind and those over ice), collard greens, country-style steak, and Carolina pulled pork, The Citadel and Azalea festivals, then bless your heart, this story is definitely for you!

According to the Wilmington Star News, the body was found almost by accident. An out-of-state driver blew a rear tire and coasted to a stop on the roadside toward the Town of Minsville. The newspaper, citing the police report, noted that had the driver not stepped out of his car and walked in the direction of a line of trees, he would have most surely missed the crumpled body lying in a shallow ditch with a blue baseball cap, garage overalls, and a face severely bludgeoned beyond recognition.

The sleepy town of Minsville, North Carolina, lies just off US Rt—40 and the Shiloh Road between Watha and Ivanhoe. If you're too busy studying your road map, texting, or just plain speeding to get to the beach, well, chances are awfully good you'd miss the well-worn sign for Historic Minsville, 1768, population 1,040 and just under that, another sign "Gas up now! Next station 50 miles." Minsville found its place in history long ago as the birthplace of one Jeremiah Paxton, loving son of the Confederacy and well-known marauder who, with his rag-tag mounted company of rebels, had repeatedly and successfully bushwhacked the Union column on their approach to the City of Wilmington. Paxton's hit-and-run tactics were effective, but as a leader, he was considered ruthless and downright mean, which was the opinion of his men. The Union army had a sizable purse on his head, dead or alive, and Paxton's luck inevitably ran out in March 1865 when Colonel Henry Hudson Mason of New Hampshire captured him. Paxton's location had come to Mason's attention thanks largely to a carefully developed local informant from Paxton's hometown of Minsville. Just who provided the information and why remains shrouded in mystery with speculation ranging from revenge and greed to unrequited love.

History books will detail that Paxon and his band of rebels soon found themselves surrounded by overwhelming Union forces and surrendered following a heavy exchange of gunfire. On the orders of Commanding General Henry Slocum, there were to be no prisoners. However, Colonel Mason took Paxon and three of his senior officers into town, where they were hung from a large American chestnut tree hovering over Minsville's beautiful town square. On Mason's orders, the bodies were left there to hang under the punishing Carolina sun until Mason and his troops left. Their bloated, putrid remains were buried behind the First Baptist church in the little graveyard under an old Magnolia tree.

Years later, the proud citizens of Minsville unanimously decided on a statue to commemorate their local hero, Jeremiah Paxton, who had fought so bravely against the invading Union army. And so, a statue was duly commissioned and erected in the town square. It was an impressive statue. There was Paxton, his saber held high, almost defiantly, and mounted on a horse with its forelegs raised high in the air. Paxon's name was inscribed in marble surrounded by oak leaf clusters with the inscription *Weep, for Richer Blood Was Never Shed*, from the grateful citizens of Minsville, North Carolina 1885." It was a fitting tribute for Minsville's local hero, who, like many, had fought and perished in that epic and bloody war between the states.

History is deeply rooted in the South, and folks from these parts take their heritage seriously, no more so than in the inhabitants of the little town of Minsville. Every year in May, for as long as the oldest resident can recall, that would be Mr. Jameston, now ninety-two, Minsville has celebrated its proud heritage and, of course, their favorite son, with a fine parade up Paxton Street starting from one end, by the old, abandoned pickle factory and ending at the statue of Jeremiah Paxton, the town square and nearby City Hall. Mayor Earl Henderson has been the Grand Marshall and has led the parade for the last twenty years; he has no plans on stepping down any time soon. The Mayor, or just plain "Earl" when he's not busily officiating as the honorable town mayor, runs Earl's Garage and Towing Service, which is right on the edge of town and, like the sign says, the one he put out on the road, "Gas up now! Next station 50 miles." However, with the new highway, any out-of-towners in Minsville are either lost or looking for a gas station. If you took part in the parade honoring Paxton, then there's a good chance you would have seen almost everything there was to see in Minsville by the time you reached the town square.

The barber shop faces the square, but its red and white barber pole stopped turning long ago. You can still get a haircut but with some advance notice. Stop at "Doc" Johnson's Drug Store and Malt Shop. If Doc's not too busy yakking someone's ear off, he will tell whoever is at the counter enjoying a malt that he'd be right back. He would personally escort you to his barber shop, slap his hand on the well-worn, cracked leather barber chair, and tell you, as he has for so many years, "Now, young man, you just sit right here and tell me how short you want that crew cut." To Doc, everyone's a young man, and age doesn't matter. Truth be told, no one knows why they even call him "Doc." he's certainly not on anyone's emergency speed dial, but aside from that little medical "detail" and one that's often overlooked, "Doc" dispenses everything from homespun medical advice, aspirin, Alka-Seltzer and Pepto-Bismol to boot shine, shoe laces, hair pomade, and lady's hairnets. One thing's for sure: "Doc" can fix one of the finest milkshakes on this side of the Mason-Dixon line.

He will be the first to tell you about when people would line up outside his drug store on a hot summer day to wait their turn to sit at his counter for a malt, milkshake, or ice cream soda. Behind the counter are his two Sealtest ice cream freezers containing those familiar varieties: vanilla, cheery-vanilla, butter pecan, chocolate, and maybe a sherbet or two, but it's a rare event when that happens—no need to get too fancy. What worked well thirty years ago should work just as well in the next thirty. Ask for a vanilla malt, one of my favorites, and "Doc" will talk your ear off as he scoops out the ice cream from a frozen tub and into the shaker, along with a casually dispensed amount of malt. He will pour the delicious frozen mixture into a large glass and set the shaker beside you. It's a meal in itself. This is something he's been doing for years, just like his father. Word of caution: if you happen to be a stranger in these parts and find yourself at his counter, do yourself a real favor and order a shake. And you won't be disappointed but expect to be asked twenty questions; after all, you're a stranger in town, and Minsville doesn't get too many of those.

The Roxy Theater has been closed for some time; no one knows how long. Most people can recall lines around the block for great movies like Gone With The Wind or maybe Ben-Hur. Beyond that, well, memories seem to fade. There's still a ratty chair in the ticket booth as if waiting for the next matinee and the arrival of the lone attendant. Inside, the rows of moth-eaten, red velveteen chairs with their sinking seats are somehow still there, bolted to the floor forever. Despite falling paint chips around a large stain, the ornate ceiling seems to hold for the moment. The city was going to look into it at some point. The Mayor, blessed with one bright idea, formed an official committee to evaluate options for the Roxy. Members included Earl, aka the Mayor, "Doc" and "Little" Johnny Marsden. They even went so far as to convince a well-known architect from Wilmington to present his design ideas for renovating the theater, perhaps even as a community center. Nothing happened after the first two meetings, not even the architect's promised payment. The whole idea just died down quietly, like many things. It was indeed a good idea, but time had overtaken the town of Minsville.

Across the street from the Roxy is Marsden's Grocery Store. It's one of those places that have never really changed, you know, the kind I mean with its painted, peeling grey steps, green swinging screen doors that slam shut, and that unmistakable smell, a combination of ripening fruit and vegetables with the tell-tell smell of an old refrigerator case and it's failing cooling system. Stepping inside is like stepping back into history. "Little" Johnny Marsden, now well into his seventies, runs the store on regular hours, six days a week, just like his father and grandfather before him. Marsden's still has a soda pop dispenser in the corner with a dusty case of Coca-Cola empties sitting on top, waiting for the next to never pickup; "I called the company in Atlanta myself," Marsden would tell inquiring customers "told me they'd be here with a delivery just as soon as they could." Over by the ornate antique register is a dusty glass case with a crack that's been there for years; once taped over as a safety precaution now, the paper is curled and yellowed. Inside the case on the top shelf, you can find a selection of King Edward Cherry Wood Tipped cigars in boxes of five and pipe tobacco in Burley and Cherry Delight, both in dusty, aged-looking pouches. On the lower shelf, just about knee-high level, are jars of hard candy, jawbreakers, rock candy, lemon drops, root beer barrels, licorice shoelaces, and more. Everything seems frozen in time as if waiting for that rush of little boys and girls running up the steps, slamming the screen door shut, and all gathering to stare at the candy case, touching the glass or pointing to their favorites. Who among them will find a few pennies or maybe even a nickel? You gotta share, promise?

Minsville Town Hall

All of "little" Johnny Marsden's ancestors proudly fought for the Confederacy and saw action at Hatteras Inlet, Roanoke Island, Richmond, and Gettysburg. He's more than willing and eager to show off a few cameos of his ancestors, innocent young faces staring back shyly yet clearly very proud in their dress grey uniforms with little knowledge of the horrors and butchery ahead of them on the field of battle. Ask "little" Johnny to show you his flag, and he will gladly bring out a replica of a Confederate battle flag, which remains carefully preserved and ready for the next time. Gone but not forgotten.

Minsville's Town Hall was once considered the crown jewel, the very definition of antebellum elegance with its ornate columns, lush gardens, and a perfect view of the fountain in the town square and the monument of Jeremiah Paxton. At one time, folks would take the detour getting off the interstate to gawk like tourists and snap pictures. The town hall was constructed originally as a residence in the early 1800s by a well-respected doctor for his beloved wife and ten children. Initially a doctor, he soon turned to the business of tar and turpentine and made a fortune. What paintings or historical descriptions of the grand home depict a graceful three-story residence with an ornate dome and a handsome wrap-around porch with large floor-to-ceiling windows that opened out, serving as porch doors? The grounds were beautifully kept with Geraniums, Azaleas, Impatiens, Dogwoods, and Begonias, all adding grace and southern charm to a beautiful home. All as it should be. Today, the stately home, known as the Minsville Municipal Town Hall, has seen better days. That's the charitable description.

The mayor, his wife, and a family of three boys and two hunting dogs live on the first and second floors as the third floor is no longer structurally sound, nor, for that matter, is the cupola. Of course, there are stories of the haunted home, though no one has yet had a confirmed sighting. Last year, one of the mayor's boys climbed up into the cupola and crashed right down to the floor below, breaking his leg in two places and just about scaring everybody half to death. It was a while before the nearest paramedic could even get there. However, one story is told that the City of Minsville never made it onto the county's new digitized maps, and the paramedics had to stop at least once and ask for directions. Outside by the gardens is a smaller structure once believed to have been the slave quarters but is now used as an off-site storage facility and equipment repair for Earl's Garage. What was once a garden overflowing with multicolored flowers has been dutifully replaced with a simple public vegetable garden courtesy of the Mayor of Minsville. It was a well-meaning gesture from the mayor's wife, and all the citizens were welcome to plant and share, but there was little evidence of any plantings in that rock-hard Carolina dirt.

Just down the road is the Stars 'n Bars Family Eatery. That would be Miss Edson's place, the most recent owner and a proud daughter of the Confederacy. She claims, eager to show anyone who would doubt her lineage, faded pictures of herself as a little girl standing in front of an ornate iron fence surrounding a stately antebellum home remarkably similar to images of the Minsville's mansion turn town hall. She can even show you a picture of her grandmama as a child sitting on the lap of an aged, white-bearded Confederate veteran. The eatery has undergone several changes, from being a rooming house in the 1800s to serving as staff headquarters for Colonel Mason during the Jeremiah Paxton episode. It had been a pool hall, then a speak-easy, rooming house with a bar on the first floor, eventually becoming a family eatery. These days, the Stars 'n Bars Family Eatery is only open on weekends, serving one sitting at 7 PM. The menu items are few, but it's genuine southern style with beaten biscuits, collard greens, ham or chicken fried steak and gravy, sides of grits, okra, and black-eyed peas, and of course, bread pudding, all washed down with sweet tea served from faded red plastic pitchers.

The Wilmington Star News followed up on an earlier reported story of a body found lying in the shallow ditch off U.S. 40. The body was identified as belonging to Jack Paxton, a vagrant of no fixed address. Earl Henderson, long-time mayor of Minsville, confessed to the brutal slaying of Jack Paxton and is now waiting for sentencing in the District Court for New Hanover County. No family members have come forth to claim the body. According to a police statement, the deceased had been working as a grease monkey at Earl's Garage and Towing Service and sleeping in a garage shed behind the town hall. The Town of Minsville is currently looking for a new mayor. "Little" Johnny Marsden is considering the position.

Things don't change much around these parts.

Dog Days in Court
Part I – The Incident

Louie, Esq. Senior Partner (AI)

Louie, Bella, Baxter & Raise, Attorneys at Law

Once the initial uproar faded and the pundits had exhausted their commentary, more astute observers began to see the case for what it truly was: a legal battle poised to become a landmark case in District Court animal jurisprudence. Their assessment was likely accurate, and it seemed inevitable that law students would be dissecting its complexities for years to come.

One seasoned commentator who had followed the case described it as the ultimate American "dogfight"—a clash between two law firms as different as night and day, where only one could emerge victorious.

So, where were the battle lines drawn in this high-stakes legal duel? On one side stood the venerable, old-guard firm of Louie, Bella, Baxter & Raise, Attorneys-at-Law—revered as the go-to experts for complex litigation. Leading the defense was the firm's senior partner, Mr. Louie, a renowned advocate for animal rights, a law professor at a prestigious university, and a trusted advisor to key figures in past administrations. With a distinguished roster of clients, Louie's reputation preceded him. His impeccable style was equally notable—his trademark white mane flowing elegantly around his shoulders. In the courtroom, he was a force of nature: eloquent, sharp, and relentless in his pursuit of truth and justice.

On the opposing side, the plaintiff was represented by Dewey Bytem & How Attorneys-at-Law. Leading their team was Mr. Dewey, a senior partner well-versed in courtroom proceedings. Dewey had earned his reputation as a tough, no-nonsense attorney, clawing his way up from the backstreets with a style as scrappy as it was effective. In his early days, he'd built his career chasing fire trucks and strays, navigating alleyways filled with poor children and tramps. Even now, he looked like a dog perpetually hungry, a survivor of hard times. A case of mange, it was whispered, had left him with an unmistakable roughness, a lingering reminder of his less fortunate years.

Mr. Dewey had all the charm of a seasoned car salesman, always angling for the next deal, ready to entertain any angle that might clinch a victory. He championed "the truth, the whole truth, and nothing but the truth"—as long as it aligned with his worldview. His firm's methods had not gone unnoticed; more than once, Dewey and his team had drawn the scrutiny of the Dogs at Law Board for questionable, if not outright unethical, practices. Yet Dewey was no fool—he was sharp and savvy and always brought his streetwise instincts into the courtroom, never hesitating to show his teeth when the situation demanded.

But before delving deeper into the case, let's rewind and fill in some essential details.

On the side of the defense stood the boutique law firm of Louie, Bella, Baxter, & Raise Attorneys-at-Law. Unlike Dewey's firm, this smaller firm was selective with its clientele, choosing cases that matched their rigorous standards. Senior partner Louie held the final say on which cases they would take, but the firm was known for its lively debates among partners, which often resembled a pack of wild dogs fighting over a bone. In this instance, junior partners Bella and Baxter and associate attorney Raise presented the facts surrounding the case: *Max v Missy.*

Bella began her summary: "On July 4th, at approximately 7:30 AM, the defendant, Max, set off on his usual patrol through the neighborhood. He conducted his routine checks, sniffing out any areas that seemed out of place or unfamiliar. The defendant insists that while walking past 4645 Elm Street, he was minding his own business, 'merely sniffing,' when an enraged white poodle named Missy, complete with a large pink bow and a partly shaved midsection, confronted him. According to Max, Missy began taunting him and snarling, much to the amusement of her owner.

Max maintains that the poodle leaped toward him threateningly, forcing him to react defensively. His jaws parted—not to bite, he claims—but in self-defense, bracing for what he believed was an imminent attack..."

At this point, confusion remains. The defendant alleges that Missy's owner intervened with a large size thirteen boot aimed directly at Max's head. According to the police report, Missy claimed she was severely traumatized by Max's threatening manner to bite her and felt her life was threatened.

Bella paused briefly to lap from the water bowl, with Raise joining her for a quick sniff. Having missed breakfast, Louie unwrapped a bone-shaped cookie, leaving it on the table while he rummaged through his briefcase. When he turned back, his treat had vanished. Sitting next to him, Baxter licked his lips, coughed, and then turned, showing Louie his rear. Louie could have snapped, but what was the point? Besides, that fruity cookie never sat well in his stomach anyway. Soon, it would be Baxter's turn to pay the price.

Bella continued, "The plaintiff—Missy—is suing for one million dollars in damages and a lifetime supply of canned dog food and biscuits. She is claiming medical expenses and emotional trauma. Missy's owner says she now refuses to walk in the neighborhood or near Elm Street, leading her to relieve herself indoors. Moreover, Missy lost her prize-winning pink ribbon during the alleged assault by the defendant."

At this last point, snorts of approval echoed around the conference room, with paws slapping in high-fives across the table. Tails wagged enthusiastically. "Way to go, Max! I like him already! It's about time someone stood up! Yes, sir, that's what I'm talking about!"

Louie, peering over his glasses, raised a well-groomed paw. "Please, can we finish this? Then we can all go outside. I know some of us need a break." His eyes lingered on Baxter, who was becoming more uncomfortable by the minute.

Attorneys Baxter and Raise then noted that the plaintiff's lawyers, Dewey, Bytem, & How Attorneys-at-Law, had filed a motion, and a preliminary court hearing date was set. At the mention of Dewey's firm, Louie shook his head, wiped his nose, and scratched himself discreetly. If there ever was a firm that built its reputation skating on thin legal ice, claiming to fight for justice in the name of dogs, it was this one.

Anyone who had ever seen a TV knew Dewey's voice and his pack of ragged hounds. Their never-ending commercials barked about one dog-related injustice after another. "Every self-respecting dog has the right to address their grievances in a court of law," Dewey would say, "no matter how small or petty those grievances might be." Louie mused that it was a noble argument if you liked ambulance-chasing dog catchers.

He could hear Dewey's latest pitch: "Have you or another dog been bitten recently? Have you taken the wrong medicine? Were you left outside for more than 24 hours? Still using the same water bowl you came home with? Were you read your rights before Animal Control locked you up? Call us, and we'll have a lawyer at your paw today!" Dewey and his pack never turned their noses up at a case—any case. And once they got their teeth into it, everything was fair game, including their client's wallet.

Given the case's merits, the partners unanimously agreed to represent the defendant. Baxter and Raise were itching to go up against Dewey, Bytem, and How in court, practically salivating at the thought. In their office, they kept a stash of "sticks and balls," their quirky metaphor for legal maneuvers, eager to finally put them to use. The decision was made, and they all went out for a quick jog to shake off the tension. Louie watched them from his window, his stiff joints preventing him from joining. He'd have to call his doctor about it tomorrow.

The following afternoon, at the uptown offices of Louie, Bella, Baxter, and Raise Attorneys-at-Law—conveniently located at West 56th and Main—Max, the defendant, was ushered into Mr. Louis' impeccably decorated office. Max shuffled in, dressed in sweatpants and a worn jacket, breathing heavily. "Man, it's hot out there! Never seen heat like this," he muttered as he flopped down in one of the leather side chairs, sniffing it before nodding in approval. He spun in the chair twice before settling in. "Look, it just happened. I don't know what got into me. Sure, I've thought about biting the dame, but who hasn't? I didn't mean to hurt her or the weird-smelling owner who held the leash. So yeah, I'm innocent! When did thinking about something bad become a crime, huh?"

With his usual calm demeanor, Louis removed his bifocals and wiped them carefully with a tissue. He placed them on the desk beside a neat stack of yellow legal pads and his prized Mont Blanc fountain pen. His desk, as always, was meticulously organized, down to the silver-framed picture of his beloved human and a candid shot of them enjoying the outdoors.

"Max," Louis began gently, "if I may call you Max, would you like some water? There's a bowl in the corner for visitors. If not, why don't you start from the beginning and tell me exactly what happened—in your own words." He leaned back in his chair, closing his eyes to listen intently.

Max sighed and began, "Yeah, sure thing. So, I was doing my usual thing, you know? Minding my own business, sniffing around for anything interesting. That's my gig. Look at these long ears—what else am I gonna do, right? Anyway, out of nowhere, this little white dog comes prancing over with a pink bow in her hair, acting all high and mighty. The worst thing they ever did was make dogs like that. I mean, come on. I ignored her, you know? I'm not getting involved in that mess. But then, she starts yapping, you know what I mean, and snarling like she owns the whole street. Her owner thinks it's funny and gives her more leash. She charges at me, and I figure I would lunge forward and show her my teeth to scare her off. But no, she lunges at me, and right then, her owner forcibly pushes me away. I squeezed between the owner's legs, and I escaped, fearing for my life. And that's how it went down. I swear. Oh, and by the way, I've got a chronic back condition too!"

Later, in Courtroom Nine, the Bailiff—an overstuffed figure clad in a blue jacket and striped pants—shuffled to the front, bellowing, "All rise! Hear ye, hear ye, the U.S. District Court of Maryland is now in session. The honorable Judge Grey Hound presiding. All those with business before this honorable court, draw near and be heard. God save the United States of America!"

"Plaintiff, you may call your first witness..."

Dog Days in Court
Part II – The Trial

District Court, Courtroom Nine, was packed to capacity. Reporters jostled for position in the front two rows, cameras clicking, elbows sharp as they vied for the best vantage point.

Dewey, representing the plaintiff, rose to his feet. "Your Honor, the plaintiff calls Doctor Athena to the stand."

Athena moved slowly, joints stiff, tail coiled carefully in his left hand as he raised his right paw to solemnly swear the oath. Dewey, resplendent in red suspenders and a new bow tie—one that, according to a style reporter later, was battery-operated with lights—approached the stand, wearing a grin that could mean only one thing: he smelled an easy win.

"Doctor Athena," Dewey began, his tone warm, as though speaking to an old friend or an unsuspecting opponent, "you specialize in deviant animal behavior, is that correct?"

Athena coughed lightly, wiped his mouth with his paw, and nodded. "Yes."

"Do you know the defendant?" Dewey asked, almost gently. "And if so, how?"

"I'm a specialist in dysfunctional dog behavior, particularly cases leading to biting incidents. Four years ago," Athena paused, pointing his tail at the defendant, "I testified in a case where he bit an esteemed public official."

Dewey's eyes gleamed. "A public official? Could you be more specific, Doctor?"

Athena straightened, his voice taking on a note of anger. "A longstanding employee of the United States Canine Mail Service Corps! One of their best, mind you, and he bit him! It's disgraceful! An outrage, even—"

"Thank you, Doctor," Dewey interrupted smoothly, puffing his chest with satisfaction. "No further questions, Your Honor."

The audience stirred, a ripple of murmurs spreading through the courtroom. Then, from the back, a voice rang out, "Hey, that's no crime—that's just good dog work if you ask me!"

The gavel came down with a resounding crack. "Order in the court!" barked the judge. "One more outburst, and you'll be leashed and dragged from this courtroom, tail between your legs!"

Jude Grey Hound (AI)

Judge Grey Hound sat back, adjusting his wig as it slid slightly out of place. How many years had he been doing this? Too many to count, even if his mind were as sharp as it used to be. Once a sanctuary of justice, the courtroom now felt more like a circus, a mockery of the law. He was too old for this. Millie wanted him home more often, and he agreed with her. It was time to let the younger legal pups handle the riffraff. It's just too many years.

His gaze returned to the courtroom, where silence waited for his direction.

"Does the Defense wish to cross-examine?" he asked, his voice rasping through a bout of coughing.

Standing at the defense table, Louie sifted through his notes before pausing dramatically. "I have just one question for the witness, Your Honor." He turned to the witness. "Doctor, are you a licensed medical professional authorized to practice in this state?"

Athena, a graying, dignified hound, leaned forward, eyes flashing. "I've been practicing longer than you've been chewing on dog bones!"

Louie gave a slight, respectful bow. "I'm sure that's evident. But the question remains unanswered..."

Athena's paws twitched in annoyance. "Listen, young pup, don't think you can outsmart me. I have an international license from the Assembly of Four-Legged Friends in Geneva, Switzerland. Recognized worldwide, including most states in this country!"

Louie turned to the jury, raising an eyebrow. "Perhaps. But not in this state. No further questions, Your Honor."

The courtroom murmured as Athena shot up from his seat. "That was a trick question! You don't know what you're talking about!"

Judge Hound waved his paw dismissively. "You may step down, Doctor."

Dewey, the plaintiff's attorney, stood next. "Your Honor, the plaintiff calls Max Tweeds to the stand."

The room stilled, tension thick in the air. This was the moment everyone had been waiting for—the heart of the case.

"Give 'em hell, Dewey!" growled an old dog from the gallery in a worn mailman's jacket. "Show 'em dogs can't go around biting decent, law-abiding pups!"

Judge Grey Hound barked, "Bailiff, get that dog out of my courtroom!" He wiped his nose with a swift motion. "I warned you all—this is my courtroom, and I won't tolerate that behavior. Anyone else cares to test me?"

He glanced around the room, then shifted his gaze to the defense. "You may proceed with your cross-examination, Mr. Dewey."

Dewey approached the stand, wiping a runny eye with his sleeve. He made two quick turns and leaned close to Max, his voice low and husky. "Max, have you ever bitten anyone before this incident?"

Max straightened. "Of course not! What kind of dog do you think I am?"

"A simple yes or no will suffice," Judge Grey Hound interrupted, his bloodshot eyes narrowing at Max.

Max exhaled. "Then no, Your Honor. I've never bitten anyone before."

Dewey leaned in more closely, revealing a grim smile, his yellowed teeth sharp beneath grey, unhealthy gums. "Are you sure about that? May I remind you that you're under oath? Let me help you with your memory."

He turned toward the judge. "Your Honor, I'd like to introduce State's Exhibit 5: A report from Gruff Animal Control, stating they were called out for a 410—an animal disturbance involving a dog bite. The dog in question? None other than the defendant, Max!"

Dewey shot a triumphant look at Louie as if smelling blood in the air. He slid toward the jury. "Ladies and gentlemen, doesn't this establish a clear deviant behavior pattern? And who's to say he won't repeat it? Next time, it could have deadly consequences."

Louie shot up from his seat. "Objection, Your Honor! That question is argumentative, assumes facts not in evidence, and calls for speculation."

Judge Grey Hound didn't hesitate. "Sustained. The jury will disregard Mr. Dewey's last statement."

Dewey grinned—it had been worth a shot. His team gave him a few congratulatory high-fives. He didn't care that the statement was stricken; the damage was done. He was a master at working a courtroom into a frenzy. Even Louie would admit that. But Dewey had the kind of sleazy demeanor that made you want to wash your hands after shaking his paw. Who knew where that paw had been?

Back at the stand, Max mumbled something barely audible. Dewey's ears perked up, and he leaned in again, his face almost touching Max's. "What was that? Speak up for the court, please."

Max cleared his throat. "Your Honor, I was involved in a biting incident—years ago, when I was just a pup. I smelled questionable mail being delivered and didn't want it in my house. But I've changed. I've paid my debt to society and become a better dog."

"No further questions, Your Honor," Dewey said, retreating with a sly grin as he oiled his way back to his table.

Does the defense wish to cross-examine?

Louie wiped his glasses methodically, then glanced up and asked, "Would you please state your profession for the court?"

Max cleared his throat, standing a little straighter. "Certainly. I assist dogs with poor eyesight and weak hips."

Louie raised an eyebrow, leaning forward slightly. "Is that all?"

Max shook his head. "No, sir. I also assist my Minister with Sunday services. In the afternoons, I mentor three young dogs on the other side of town as their 'Big Dog.' And on Christmas Eve, I help wrap gifts for underprivileged dogs."

Louie turned to the jury, a playful smile tugging at the corner of his mouth. "A true menace to society, as you can see." He chuckled softly, adding, "No further questions, your Honor."

Plaintiff, Missy La Rue

The plaintiff's team then called Missy La Rue. A hush fell over the courtroom as the guards swung open the heavy doors. At that exact moment, Missy made her grand entrance as if stepping into her long-awaited Oscar moment. Every detail had been meticulously curated by her team of trial experts, all with one goal: a head-to-toe explosion of pink. From her dainty pillbox hat, with its delicate veil draping over her graying nose, to her towering pink stilettos, Missy was a spectacle.

Careful research had shown that pink, a cheerful and "feel good" color, would work in her favor given the jury's demographics, the time of day, and even the average temperature in courtrooms. Missy teetered down the aisle toward the witness stand, leaving a trail of cloying, sickly-sweet perfume that could only have come from the drugstore shelves. Observers later recalled how some in the gallery discreetly pulled out handkerchiefs, covering their noses and mouths to shield themselves from the overwhelming fumes.

With the grace of a beauty queen without her Miss Poodle sash, Missy paraded past the jury box, flashing a smile at the jurors and then another at the judge, who had now perched his glasses on his nose, clearly intrigued by this peculiar vision. After much fidgeting, turning, and an exaggerated flourish, Missy finally settled into the witness chair. She opened her oversized purse, pulled out a compact mirror, adjusted a stray lock of hair, and reapplied a bold swipe of pink lipstick.

For a brief moment, the courtroom was utterly silent. Mouths hung open, tongues practically resting on the floor, and more than a few sharp elbows nudged ribs. It was a moment frozen in time, as some would later say—you could have heard a pin drop.

Dewey slowly approached Missy, his eyes scanning her as he drew closer. She looked good—really good—and he made a conscious effort to keep his tongue from practically hitting the floor. Missy, noticing his attention, blushed as Dewey circled her, not once, but twice.

"My dear Madam," Dewey began, oiling charm from every pore, his tone smooth and calculated. "This has been a dreadful ordeal for you, and I'm sure the court recognizes that. If you can, please—for the sake of the jury—share, in your own words, the sequence of events that left you so emotionally traumatized."

Missy was more than ready for this moment. She'd rehearsed this question with Dewey countless times, and he wasn't just a sharp lawyer—he was her type, too. She carefully removed her chewing gum, placing it delicately on a piece of paper, which she handed to the Bailiff.

"Well," she began, her voice dripping with theatrical flair," I was minding my own business. I had on a new outfit and my pink pageant bow, which, you know, has a very special meaning for me. And then, out of nowhere, this filthy creature comes slinking towards me—beastly, unkempt, hair all in knots!" Missy shuddered dramatically. "I swear, I smelled wine on his breath, and it was morning! Pathetic. I'm a cosmetologist, and this hairstyle—" she gestured at her perfectly coiffed locks—"doesn't come cheap, let me tell you."

Missy's eyes widened as she continued, leaning into the drama of her tale. "Anyway, he was heading right for me, smelling like he hadn't bathed in weeks, and I guess it was just instinct—self-preservation, you know? I told him to back off the sidewalk! If I'd had my nail file, I might have used it, too. He was monstrous, leering at me with drool hanging from his mouth. He was down low, his ears dragging in the mud!"

The jury exchanged puzzled glances, but Missy was on a roll. "Two days ago, I saw him again, leering at me—and get this, he peed right where I always walk! I can't go back to that spot ever again! What kind of awful animal does that, Mister Prosecutor Sir?"

A few stifled giggles broke out in the courtroom. The jurors exchanged knowing winks, and even the ordinarily stoic Judge Grey Hound couldn't wholly suppress a grin. He restored order with a sharp rap of his gavel, though one court reporter later claimed he'd seen the judge smile.

"Does the Defense wish to cross-examine?"

Louie rose from his seat, his eyes briefly scanning his notes before locking onto the witness. He approached the stand, his voice calm yet deliberate. "I want to thank you for making the effort to be here this morning," he began, the faintest edge of sarcasm lacing his words. Missy, oblivious, gave a polite nod and absentmindedly patted her hair, completely missing the growing tension in the room.

"Madam," Louie continued, raising a folder, "in my hand, I hold medical records, a doctor's evaluation, and the report from that fateful day—documents that shed light on the event you claim left you so deeply traumatized." He flipped open the report with a theatrical pause. "The doctor's review states: 'Over three days of observation, no evidence was found linking the subject's psychological trauma to recent events. However, there is neck trauma, likely the result of repeated pulling and jerking of a pink leash and collar. It is entirely plausible that this injury was caused by human action rather than by a dog or any other animal.'"

Missy's face paled as she fumbled into her oversized bag. With shaky hands, she pulled out a comb and began nervously running it through her pink hair, her agitation palpable.

Louie took a step back. "No further questions, Your Honor."

Dog Days in Court
Part III – The Day of Reckoning

The Shaping of Hearts and Minds

*L*ong before the first gavel struck in Courtroom Number Nine, the case's merits had already ignited fierce debates on the airwaves, in newspapers, and across every Sunday talk show. Some called it a veritable "feast of fools." Meanwhile, high-powered public relations firms were gearing up to craft their versions of the truth across town, treating the public like lost puppies eager for direction. Who backed who was a tangled web, but one thing was clear: this was shaping up to be the dogfight of the century. The PR firms and lawyers were already eyeing summer homes in the Hamptons and on Cape Cod in celebration.

Two firms, in particular, stood at the forefront of the spin game: 2Snouts-a-Sniffing PR and Tail-Waggin Associates. These companies played pivotal roles, working closely with associations with deeper pockets and a dog in the fight. Their roster included heavyweights like the Firehouse Dog Association, the Society of Big Dogs of America, the Mail Carriers Union, the Dog Food Preparers Union, the Canned Meats Association, and their allies in the Dry Dog Food Group. Like loyal hounds on command, their representatives appeared on talk shows, reciting their version of events, spinning clever arguments to persuade even the most cynical of mutts. It was slick. It was effective.

One of the most polarizing figures in this high-stakes drama was the infamous shock jock from BYTE Radio, known as "Yo Hound Dog Daddy." With his shaggy brown curls and signature sunglasses, he howled—literally—at the beginning and end of each broadcast. The wolf-dog persona invited all manner of junkyard dogs onto his show to gnaw on the latest twists of the story. In one particularly heated segment, a guest who supported Missy found himself nose to nose with a biker dog clad in a leather vest, leaving the studio in tears. It was raw, no-holds-barred radio—if you had the stomach for Hound Dog Daddy.

Meanwhile, over at the Marrow Bone Restaurant on D Street, where the crisp white napkins stood as stiff as the clientele, the city's power brokers gathered for lunch and cocktails. Lawyers, lobbyists, PR experts, and staffers from the highest branches of government assembled in this high-powered watering hole. Louie and his legal team were regulars, holding court over bowls of bones drenched in the restaurant's signature marrow sauce. Among well-dressed, well-heeled patrons, deals were made with pats on the back, whispers, promises, and knowing winks.

For Louie, the pressure was mounting. Every day was another round of strategy discussions and client meetings. His closing argument was looming, and the jury was still unpredictable. One moment, they seemed swayed by Louie's eloquence; the next, Dewey's arguments appeared to win them over. It all came down to a delicate balance, and Louie knew he had to tip the scales in his favor. That's all it would take.

On the other side of town, a different scene played out at the Nose On Inn. Friday nights were prime time for the local band, the Bad Dog Boys, who never failed to pack the place with loyal fans. It was the kind of bar where the beer had to be ice-cold—anything less would be considered an insult. The scotch was cheap because it was unapologetically basic, and the food was fast, thanks to the microwaves working overtime. But the place was known for its sandwiches—towering creations stacked so high they defied gravity, offered at prices that couldn't be beaten anywhere in town. Cash was the only currency accepted, a policy proudly displayed in the bathroom: "In God We Trust, All Others Pay Cash."

Dewey was a regular, often showing up late with a cloud of aftershave that preceded him. He'd down a few scotches and scope the room, always looking for a new conquest. The Inn was a favorite hangout for the public safety crowd—firefighters, paramedics, and the like—which meant the clientele leaned toward the larger side. German Shepherds, Dobermans, Dalmatians, and Huskies were everywhere, and the only small dog you'd see might be what was left of it on someone's plate. Dewey and his crew would settle into their corner, holding court and plotting whatever the next day had in store.

The Day of Reckoning

Long before dawn, television vans lined up like soldiers outside the grand, century-old courthouse, antennas raised, satellite dishes locked in place. The scene was one of frantic preparation, with technicians racing to unfurl cables and set up mics, ensuring everything would be ready for when the judge's gavel dropped. Each network had sent its most polished pair of on-air talent. For WBRK, that meant Vinn Tales and a last-minute addition—"Morganna."

Vinn, freshly tanned from a grueling assignment in the Bahamas, looked sharp in a tan suit and a bold lime-green-and-pink-striped tie that highlighted his bronzed complexion. His team hovered close by, ensuring no hair was out of place. Morganna, brought in from Atlanta after Vinn's usual co-anchor fell ill, was a seasoned pro despite being known chiefly for her weather reports. She had quickly nudged out the bubbly Stormy Summers, WBRK's usual sunny persona, with a red umbrella to match. Morganna was poised and sharp on camera, effortlessly matching Vinn's banter. As they rehearsed their lines, the usual mix of irrelevant quips came out: "In a surprising twist, a dog who bites dogs on trial, but up next, we'll look at how a banana peel might be the key to your joint pain!" Smiles, laughs, camera one, fade to commercial...

It was shaping up to be one of those quintessential summer days. The sun rose like a molten orb of burnt orange, casting a scorching threat across the horizon as if intent on incinerating everything in its path. By 8 AM, the temperature had already hit a sweltering 85 degrees, with the forecast hinting at a chance of light rain—though the humidity, clocking in at a brutal 90%, made it feel like the heat was thick enough to choke. The oppressive air hung over the city, and the morning rush hour only added to the misery, as cars spewed fumes that mixed into a toxic summer haze.

By 9:00 AM, a long line had already formed outside the courthouse—placeholders paid for their patience waited for their employers to assume their spots when the doors finally opened. The real players would soon replace these stand-ins: the legal teams and their high-profile clients. Security was tight, with municipal law enforcement bolstered by a "Cop in a Box," screening every bag and briefcase through metal detectors. Two knives were confiscated, along with several cans of pepper spray, a flask of whiskey, and more than a few small bottles of vodka. Despite a ban on cameras and recording devices, some inevitably went inside, covertly streaming data to various television and radio stations.

A sleek black limousine rolled up to the curb before the courthouse steps. An eager young assistant, clearly trying to make a name for himself, jumped out to open the rear door. Louie, the defense attorney, stepped out, followed closely by Max, the defendant. Louie cut a striking figure in an expensive, custom-made dark blue chalk stripe suit, crisp white shirt, and a discreet striped tie. He paused, gold bone-shaped cufflinks glinting as he adjusted them, giving the photographers enough time to snap a few shots. "No comment," he muttered to the growing crowd of reporters, though he added, with a practiced smile, "We're optimistic, but time will tell."

Vinn and Morgana, the dynamic TV duo, pushed their microphones into the fray. Morgana, ever excitable, squeaked, "Max, how do you feel this morning? What did you have for breakfast?" Always the more calculated of the two, Vinn aimed straight at Louie. "Is this case make-or-break for your legal career? Are you considering a run for public office?" Louie offered a calm smile, dodging the question as the crowd swarmed up the courthouse steps—a sea of flashing cameras and frenzied voices. Behind them, the defense team trailed with the gravity of a procession, each member carrying two bulging briefcases—the collective brain trust of the operation.

No sooner had Louie and Max disappeared into the courthouse than a stretch white limousine pulled up to the curb. Instantly, the swarm of TV crews, lights, and cameras shifted to the new arrival. Dewey, the prosecutor, emerged first, looking sharp in a black suit, black shirt, and silver-white tie. With a practiced air of calm, he turned and helped Missy, the media's darling, out of the car. Missy was the woman every social editor was desperate to profile, her story tantalizingly elusive. Today, her image consultants had gone for a striking look: a pure white ensemble, bridal in its simplicity. Gone was her signature pink, though one sharp-tongued editor whispered that surely there was a trace remaining in an undisclosed location.

Dewey, never one to rush, gave the press just enough to keep them on the hook, answering questions without saying anything. But that didn't matter—he had mastered feeding the media just enough to stretch a nothing statement into two minutes of air time. "We've just learned the prosecution plans to..." teased a reporter, setting up the next wave of speculation.

"Stay tuned for more updates on this sensational case and a look back at Dewey's meteoric rise from car salesman to prosecution attorney."

The TV crews were preparing their next broadcast as the crowd jostled for the next scoop. "Live from the courthouse steps," Vinn announced into the camera, "I'm Vinn Tales." Morgana followed with her practiced smile, "And I'm Morgana. More news and the weather coming up at the top of the hour!"

Dog Days in Court
Part IV – Closing
Arguments and Verdict

The Bailiff, her powder blue jacket straining at the seams and striped pants clinging to her as she sweated in the stifling courtroom, shuffled toward the front of a packed Courtroom No. 9. "All rise! Hear ye, hear ye, the U.S. District Court of Maryland is now in session, the Honorable Judge Grey Hound presiding. All those with business before this honorable court, draw near, give your attention, and you shall be heard. God save the United States of America!"

"Mr. Dewey, as the Plaintiff, your closing argument, if you please."

Dewey patted Missy gently before standing to address the jury. This was it—now or never. "Just think of it like selling a lemon of a car to some poor fool," he thought, shaking off the nerves. He scanned the jurors, pretending to meet each face for the first time. The barrel-chested one with the long mutton chops in the back row had nodded off repeatedly during the trial. That other juror, sausage-like and wobbling on two paws, seemed to stir only for Missy. The front row was better, thankfully. A few attractive jurors were seated there, flanked by a large black lab with graying whiskers and a permanent drool problem.

Still, Dewey exhaled, placed one paw casually on the bench, and inhaled deeply, sniffing the air to find his connection with the jury. He began.

"Distinguished jury members, we've endured a long and tiresome journey together. I know it hasn't been easy for any of you. But today, I stand before you with one simple truth—one the defense has bent over backward to muddy, to distort. You've heard the testimony. You've listened to witnesses recount, with heartbreaking detail, the defendant's history of aggravated, unprovoked biting.

"Ladies and gentlemen, unless decent, law-abiding citizens like you act, this menace will continue. It will bite again—helpless little dogs, senior dogs in their twilight years, dogs of every breed and stripe. The security of your neighborhoods, the peace of your homes—it's all at risk. So, I leave you with this: the safety of dogs everywhere now lies in your hands. Thank you."

Dewey sat down, his tail flicking once, as the jury considered the weight of their decision.

"Mr. Louie, for the defense," Judge Grey Hound announced.

Louie stood up, confidently pushing away from the defense table. He strode purposefully toward the jury box, speaking as he approached.

"Ladies and Gentlemen of the jury, you've just heard the plaintiff's version of events—a narrative skillfully woven with innuendos, half-truths, and inconsistencies. Their timeline of events is chaotic, their witnesses questionable, and their so-called 'facts' flimsy at best. Mr. Dewey wants you to believe my client is some menace worthy of imprisonment and, perhaps, to be forgotten in the public pound. He even suggests that Missy, their star witness, suffered emotional trauma at the hands of my client.

But let's be clear. Missy's trauma stems from far before the alleged incident. My client, Max, has been an upstanding member of society for over fifteen years. And yes, whatever happened in his youth shouldn't be a lifelong burden. Indeed, all sensible dogs can agree with that. Max has dedicated himself to public service, helping the less fortunate. He is a model citizen, and I trust that you will come to see him for who he truly is. Thank you for your time and service."

Louie sat down, and Dewey, brimming with confidence, bowed respectfully to the bench.

"Your Honor..." he began, but Judge Hound interrupted Dewey.

"I will now instruct the jury on the law. This case is in your hands," Judge Hound said, turning to the jury as he started explaining.

Some moments later, a shout was heard in the hall outside Courtroom Nine: "They're back already!"

The jury filed back into the room. Judge Hound addressed them with a firm nod. "Has a verdict been reached?"

Juror No. 5 stood up. "Yes, Your Honor, we have."

The Bailiff took the verdict slip and handed it to the judge. The judge reviewed it for legal sufficiency, nodded, and returned it to the Bailiff.

Juror No. 5 cleared his throat. "On the first count of aggravated dog attack, we find the defendant... guilty as charged."

Dewey's grin spread wide, triumph written all over his face. He shot Louie a smug look. "Who's the real attorney now?" he whispered.

Before Louie could respond, Missy leaped up from her seat, shouting, "Max is not guilty! It was all a setup from the start! I can't let an innocent dog go to prison because of lies! He's the one—" she pointed a trembling finger at the retired dog mailman in the corner—"he set this all up!"

The mailman, startled, moved toward the door. "Officers, stop that dog from leaving," Judge Hound ordered.

Two burly black labs swiftly blocked the old mailman's escape.

"It would've worked if it weren't for that damned meddling dame!" the retired dog barked bitterly. "I would've finally had my revenge!"

"Officers, take that mail dog away," the judge commanded. "This case is dismissed, and the defendant is free to go." He slammed the gavel, sealing the decision.

Barbie and Ken stood outside the courthouse with their TV crew, ready to go live.

"Well, Morganna, this trial has been a rollercoaster from start to finish," said Vinn.

"A real doozie, Vinn," Morganna replied. "We had suspense, drama, unanswered questions, and one heck of a surprise ending."

"Exactly, Morganna. Stay tuned as Suzy Lee will have more from inside the courthouse at the top of the hour. But first, here is a word from our sponsor on what you should know about nutritional labels on dog food."

Learn more about this series in *The Making of Dog Days in Court – Behind the Scenes* and *The Director's Cuts: Dog Days in Court.*

THE GREAT CONTEST

During one of those blistering Maryland summers, I received an unexpected call from a friend. She urged me to enter a writing contest organized by a women's clothing store that, perhaps out of sheer desperation amid slumping sales, had decided to dive into the jeans business. Their plan? Manufacture offshore, slap on an eye-watering price tag, and hope for a quick windfall. The prize for the contest, aptly titled *Tales of Denim*, was enough to catch anyone's attention: two round-trip tickets to

Paris. You can see why my friend was eager for me to enter, and sensing a challenge, I happily accepted, feeling like a gauntlet had been thrown.

As with all legends, they can get exaggerated over time. Supposedly, Ernest Hemingway once wrote a six-word story ("For sale: baby shoes, never worn"), which he allegedly considered his finest work. Having long admired Hemingway's larger-than-life persona and bold writing style, I found this legend captivating. The contest's task was to craft a short story, no more than six words, that featured jeans, a Parisian theme, and a touch of humor. Naturally, I couldn't resist the challenge.

There I was, relaxing on my little patio, cooling off with a glass of super-chilled Marlborough Sauvignon Blanc from New Zealand. Pen and paper in hand, waiting for inspiration to strike— but nothing. Absolutely nothing. Instead, my mind wandered to more mundane matters: I needed to buy milk, bread, and orange juice, and I had a doctor's appointment later that week. Creativity? Sorry, nowhere to be found. So, I started doodling, jotting down absurd six-word sentences to amuse myself. One of my favorites: "Take my money, leave my jeans." Before I knew it, my scratch pad was full of silly nonsense, and the moment had passed.

And then, the contest deadline arrived—along with her phone call.

"Well, dear, did you come up with something clever? I know you did. Should I start packing for Paris now?"

Thank goodness for her confidence—no pressure, right? I told her I'd concocted something unconventional that, in my mind at least, involved Paris, jeans, humor, a dash of intrigue, and, of course, a bit of *oh là là*—Parisian flair!

And so, over the phone, I shared my little creation…

"Maxim's called; they found your jeans."

There was a moment of silence on the other end.

"I don't get it," she finally replied.

I explained to her, "Now look, one has to wonder who would dare go to Maxim's, the famous restaurant in Paris, in a pair of jeans, designer or not. The sheer nerve of the lady and then to have them misplaced. What does that tell you? *Non mais Monsieur vous me prenez pour idiot?* The sheer nerve of Madame!"

"Are you following me?" I continued

"Was she French? It would explain things *un peut*. How did it happen? What did she do? Where in the restaurant did it happen? How did the unfortunate lady ever get home? Was she wearing anything else besides expensive French perfume? These were more questions than *Monsieur le Commissaire Maigret* would have asked." You can destroy a story with over-explanation. That moment may have come.

"Well, OK," she replied, "if that's your decision, it's your story." Distancing already…

I never heard back. I presume my entry was submitted and perhaps even given a passing look; I'd like to think so. Then, undoubtedly, a shake of the head: "Non, non, non…not what we're looking for." I'm sure somebody got a nice round-trip ticket to Paris. Whoever it was, it wasn't me.

It was a lousy contest, anyway. There's your short story in six words!

Ms. Edith's Travel Agency

"Paris is a place where we can forget ourselves, reinvent
ourselves, and expunge the dead weight of our past."
—Michael Simkins, *Detour de France:
An Englishman in Search of a Continental Education*

s. Edith St. Germain gently lowered a single window
blind with a perfectly manicured fingernail, the mo-
tion as precise and graceful as that of a seasoned artist. She lingered
just long enough to watch the first snowflakes drifting like tiny
white parachutes, one by one, toward the quiet street below. For a
brief moment, she watched as the pavement appeared to draw up a

soft, white blanket, erasing the world beneath in a peaceful trans-formation. They had predicted snow—Ms. Edith recalled reading it in the *Chicago Tribune*. Yet, as always, she had first consulted her horoscope, which, curiously, had made no mention of snow. The horoscope and weather forecast were her daily rituals, small but steadfast anchors, offering a sense of order and purpose—and, at the very least, something to look forward to.

As dusk settled over the city, the streetlights flickered to life, casting a soft amber glow over the snowy landscape. The street was peaceful, a December evening quieting the last murmurs of rush-hour chaos. Only a few stragglers walked by, oblivious to Ms. Edith watching above her travel agency storefront. Couples strolled arm-in-arm with their holiday packages, while a young man she recognized from the next building took his dog for an early evening walk. Now and then, a lone businessman hurried by, hunched against the biting wind, his breath visible in the cold air. Clutching his briefcase like a lifeline, he rushed toward the sta-tion, determined not to miss the last commuter train that would carry him away to the warmth and safety of the suburbs, perhaps Naperville or Buffalo Grove.

Business at the Travel Dreams Agency had been slow—excruciatingly so. There hadn't been a single inquiry that day, and the week had offered little more than the mailman dutifully delivering bills, late notices, and an onslaught of holiday advertisements. The holiday frenzy had captured everyone's attention; thoughts of glamorous getaways and distant destinations seemed far from anyone's mind. Ms. Edith's superior travel services, always at the ready, remained unnoticed. Yet, she was resolute. This would change. *Bien sûr,* she thought. It was inevitable. After the long, dreary winter, spring would come—and with it, daydreams of Paris. Who wouldn't yearn to be in Paris in the spring? The City of Lights was irresistible, and Ms. Edith believed, with unwavering conviction, that her customers would soon be back, ready to indulge in the magic she so carefully curated.

Ms. Edith St. Germain, formerly Edith Wyzgowski, a native Chicagoan, had adopted her new, more glamorous name as a *nom de plume,* inspired by the well-known *Boulevard St. Germain* in Paris's 6th arrondissement. Her agency was tucked away on the north end of Wabash Avenue, just a block from the intersection of Wabash and Belvedere, close to the rattling elevated tracks of the L. Passersby could hardly miss the large travel posters taped to her storefront window, beckoning them to explore Athens, Rome, and Bora Bora. Her favorite was crowded among the frayed posters: an oversized advertisement featuring a smiling Pan Am stewardess inviting travelers to board the Clipper jet for a direct flight from New York to Paris.

When planning trips—especially to Paris—Ms Edith was without equal. Some even claimed her expertise was unrivaled, her knowledge of the city so deep that it bordered on legendary. Her stories of Paris were vivid, drawing listeners in as if they, too, were strolling the avenues with Edith Piaf or mingling with film stars like Jean-Paul Belmondo or Cary Grant. Every tale was meticulously crafted to enchant young lovers, newlyweds, and couples dreaming of their first European trip. Her charisma and infectious enthusiasm made it impossible not to believe in her vision of Paris.

But the truth was more complicated than the stories suggested. It was Ms. Edith's mother, not Ms. Edith herself, who had once been to Paris—several decades ago- while pregnant with Ms. Edith. She had named her daughter after her dearest friend, Edith Piaf. And so, while Ms. Edith's tales of Paris were embroidered with a few harmless white lies, they were told with a passion that made them feel real. After all, what harm was there in embellishing a bit to seal a round-trip package to the City of Lights? In the grand scheme, she mused, a little creative storytelling never hurt anyone—especially when Paris was on the line. Money, after all, was money in any currency.

The snow continued to fall steadily as the evening deepened. The streets outside were now deserted, the world muffled under a thickening blanket of white. Ms. Edith cracked open her window, letting the cold rush of winter air hit her face. Quickly, she shut it again, seeking refuge in the warmth of her cozy domain. She turned to her beloved record player and carefully selected a vinyl. Soon, the haunting voice of Edith Piaf filled the room, wrapping her in nostalgia *"Il me dit des mots d'amour. Des mots de tous les jours…"* For a few moments, she was transported to another time, another place—a fleeting sense of contentment as the quiet winter night enveloped her.

WHEN ARE WE GOING
TO EAT REAL FOOD?

The following conversation may have occurred in an office along New York's Madison Avenue. Just maybe...

"Listen, Harry, I know you're the new kid here, but I'm going to tell you something from the get-go, I don't give a damn if what we're tryin' to sell is not "really" French food, 'cause Harry, "are you listening to me,

Harry?" "Tell me, who in the hell's gonna know the difference...some schmuck from Toledo? We're calling this stuff French Toast!" They're gonna buy it and think they're in Paree or wherever it is!"

On more than one occasion, I've overheard fellow countrymen abroad lamenting the absence of "real food" from back home. For many of us, "real food" is that reliable journey from freezer to microwave to the dinner table in the blink of a nano-second. There's something strangely satisfying about venturing deep into the frosty abyss of my freezer, triumphantly dragging out a box that Admiral Byrd might have as well left behind on a polar expedition. Pop it in the microwave, nuke it until it's glowing hotter than the sun—or until Homeland Security knocks on the door, whichever comes first.

Every time I find myself in Paris, I can't help but observe my compatriots' unique behavior, particularly regarding food. The frustration usually starts with those "crazy" menus—the ones that should be in English but, shockingly, are in some foreign language. I mean, who doesn't speak American these days? What gets them even more is the sight of menus scribbled in chalk, with random Euro signs scattered about like stock market tickers. And in some places, they're written on mirrors! Fancy mirrors, mind you. It's as if deciphering lunch has become a financial analysis in a funhouse.

The Restaurant

Many American tourists yearn for home while visiting Paris, and the food—or the dining experience—is often the culprit. Heads lowered, they wander the charming streets, searching for something familiar and, in their eyes, edible—perhaps something like they'd find in Duluth. When friends return from their first trip to "Paree," the complaints don't take long to surface. Gathered around a lukewarm hot dog, a slice of cherry cobbler, and a diet Sprite, they grumble. Yes, they'll mention the cramped bathrooms and showers "built for hobbits," but the conversation inevitably loops back to the food.

"The waiters! Dreadful!" they'll say, eyes wide with disbelief. "Rude, dismissive, and those ridiculous little uniforms! We practically had to tackle the guy for any attention! And when he finally bothered with us, that's when the real horror show began: The Menu."

Ah, oui, the menu. A tome filled with options—each more bewildering than the last, and all, of course, in French. Pages of daily specials, prix fixe combinations, and a dizzying array of *"apéritifs,"* which seemed to mean little more than "booze" in a little glass. There is nothing like the cozy comfort of Jack and Joan's Bistro back home on the corner of Elm and Main. Once the menu hit the table, the waiter vanished—gone, as if by magic. They were convinced he wasn't French, given his accent, but that didn't make the situation any easier. So, they resorted to a time-tested tactic: frantic waving and shouting, "Oh, garçon! Over here, for crying out loud, Harry, our guy's disappeared again. Can you flag him down?"

When the garçon finally returned, armed with a pen and an unmistakable air of impatience, he asked, *"Alors, on a décidé?"* You grasp a few familiar words: steak, salad, French fries. *"Oui*, very gourmet," you manage. Your dining companion follows with a simple, "A hamburger, please."

The unimpressed waiter flips the menu to desserts with a mixture of disappointment and mild amusement as if trying to teach a particularly slow dog a new trick.

Menus swiftly collected; he vanished again. You exhale, relieved to have seemingly survived the infamous French dining ordeal. But no.

Moments later, he glides back through the maze of cramped tables, looking even more exasperated. You're not sure what crime you've committed this time, but he gestures grandly toward the drink menu with a tight smile. His suggestion drips with sarcasm: "Coca-Cola?"

American Made French Food

The masterminds of Madison Avenue have skillfully convinced us that fine French cuisine is just a freezer door away. No need to scour the streets of Paris—reach into your freezer, and *voilà*! France comes to you right in your kitchen. From frozen delights to your dining room table, you can experience the "magic" of Paris without ever leaving your zip code. Who needs the *Champs-Élysées* when you can have "Paris in Suburbia"? *Magnifique!*

Our marketers have excelled at rebranding everyday dishes as "authentic" French cuisine, available even at your local truck stop diner. Look at the gourmet menu: French fries, French crepes, French bread, French onion soup, French ice cream—*oh là là*! And who could forget French toast, French apple pie, and that classic: "Would you like French dressing with your iceberg lettuce, hon?" It's no surprise that when the so-called "ugly American" has their first genuine taste of French food abroad, they're left puzzled. Nothing is quite how it's "supposed" to be—certainly not like the French cuisine we're used to back home.

The shock is immediate. The "fries" arrive as thin, crispy matchsticks on your plate, each exuding an air of superiority—unlike the plump, golden fries from the freezer aisle or, better yet, the ones doused in gravy. And when it comes to French toast? Instead of the towering stack of fluffy, syrup-soaked goodness you're used to, you're served two delicate slices with tiny butter pats and a stingy assortment of preserves. Where's the syrup-laden, gooey delight that could double as dessert? I miss it so.

The Baguette Weaponized

Forget the soft, pre-sliced bread often smothered in turkey gravy for sandwiches—this is not that kind of French bread. The baguette is not to be sliced or soaked in sauces. Oh no, *Monsieur*, the baguette must never suffer such indignity. If you're ever tempted to buy one—perhaps to show off to relatives back in Muncie—be warned: in just one day, that fresh loaf will transform into a hardened relic, a veritable blunt object. As countless American travelers have learned, day-old baguettes are often confiscated upon reentry into the United States.

American expats have discovered a different use for stale baguettes in Paris: baseball bats for impromptu games in the Bois de Boulogne. And it's not just sport—ask any French husband who's been too slow to listen to his wife. A swift crack on the head from a day-old baguette is a common enough occurrence that the local police have learned to turn a blind eye. These officers are wise; they know better than to interfere in baguette-related marital disputes.

A Baguette in the Mail

Some years ago, I found myself in Brittany with my adult children. My son, being the jokester that he is, decided he wanted to mail a baguette back to his office. This was part of an ongoing tradition— each time someone traveled abroad, they sent something clever and nonsensical. He offered no further explanation.

With the baguette in hand, we marched into *La Poste*, where I, as the designated spokesperson, explained the plan to the young woman behind the counter. The expression on her face was priceless—a blend of confusion and disbelief, as if she'd just realized she was dealing with an escapee from the local asylum. Sensing the situation's absurdity, the other customers slowly shook their heads in silent judgment.

The postal clerk quickly summoned her supervisor, Madame the Supervisor, for assistance. They huddled together, exchanging furtive glances in our direction as if trying to gauge just how idiotic we really were. Finally, Monsieur, the Chief Supervisor, approached us with a look that seemed to ask, "How ridiculous can you be?" He explained, with great politeness, that mailing a baguette to the United States was simply out of the question. His reason? "Monsieur, the baguette will not be fresh when it arrives."

Ah, of course—the State had spoken. Case closed.

But I wasn't ready to give up. Drawing on every ounce of charm I could muster, I assured him that freshness was no concern. I even offered to sign any legal documents required to absolve the post office, the bakery, the village, and the French State from responsibility. The only thing we asked, as silly Americans, was for them to wrap it up and send it on its way.

Finally, after much negotiation, the entire postal staff seemed to agree with our ridiculous request. The baguette was carefully wrapped in sturdy brown paper, half obscured by official French stamps. The whole post office was buzzing—smiles, giggles, and muttered comments like "*Ah, les Américains*" filled the room. I was tempted to remind them of how little they protested when American tanks rolled through in 1944, but I bit my tongue—diplomacy, after all.

Ultimately, the baguette traveled across the Atlantic, arriving at my son's office in a hardened, "weaponized" state. Freshness be damned—it was appreciated all the same. I imagined they used the baguette for batting practice somewhere on the college quad.

Real Food

When the French hit our shores, do we see them flustered, wrestling with a burger the size of a small planet? Of course not. Look again; they're already climbing the culinary ladder, carving out their meal with finesse. Do they pause at our iceberg lettuce, wondering how the Titanic's captain ever thought he could outmaneuver an iceberg? Not at all. They pick up a fork like a jackhammer and dive in without hesitation. And you won't catch them turning up their noses at a towering stack of pancakes topped with eggs, sausage links, and drenched in strawberry syrup. No way—they devour it with enthusiasm; it's all just as they'd imagined.

We must be doing something right because they keep coming back, again and again, for more of that "Yo Mama's" roadside diner experience—complete with hot (sort of) roast beef sandwiches, mashed potatoes smothered in gravy, and a frosty Root Beer to wash it all down. Ahh, *le* sweet life!

Part II

LATIN AMERICA

MEXICO
Sunday Afternoon in Mexico City

Jai Alai at the Fronton

Mexico City's airport was unusually bustling for a Sunday. After lining up for customs, I waited for my bag for an eternity. A final hurdle—the baggage scan—stood between me and my exit. At last, I emerged through international arrivals, door number 7, stepping into the hot, steamy, and unmistakably pungent air.

There's something oddly familiar about exiting airports in certain parts of the world. I've visited countries across the spectrum—from developing nations to emerging economies—and, frankly, what you see is what you get. The sharp sting of car and bus exhaust clings to the air, making your eyes water. Drivers relentlessly blare their horns, a cacophony that leaves you mentally drained before leaving the curb.

Adding to the charm, the unmistakable, sweet-sour scent of rotting fruit wafts over from the Bordo Poniente Landfill, just a stone's throw from the airport. On this particular morning, the winds from the mountains carried the landfill's fragrance straight to us. There's been talk—rumors, really—about the government building a state-of-the-art, world-renowned airport. So far, it remains just that: talk. It's a great idea if it ever comes to fruition.

Stepping out from the arrivals building, I was greeted by an unexpected soundscape—cannons booming and marching bands filling the air. Was this spectacle in my honor, I mused? Or perhaps, more alarmingly, was there a revolution brewing? I imagined soldiers gathering in the Bosque de Chapultepec, preparing to defend Los Pinos, the President's official residence. My thoughts turned briefly to a quick escape plan, just in case things took a turn for the worse.

At that very moment, a black SUV—massive and imposing—screeched to a halt in front of me. The tinted window rolled down, and instead of the gun barrel I half-expected, Eduardo, my customer, offered an apologetic grin. "Sorry for the delay—traffic's crazy. After all, it is Cinco de Mayo."

"Of course," I replied, masking my momentary lapse. How could I forget such a significant date?

It was clear this wouldn't be a lazy Sunday afternoon. "We're heading to the Fronton to catch some professional Jai Alai. Does that work for you?" he asked, though the question was rhetorical. Without waiting for my response, we sped toward Avenida de la República 17, the Fronton Mexico.

The Fronton stands proudly across from the *Plaza de la República* in the shadow of the Monument to the Revolution. This towering structure houses the remains of key figures from the Mexican Revolution, including the audacious Francisco "Pancho" Villa and the steadfast Francisco I. Madero. Curiously, Emiliano Zapata, another revolutionary giant, isn't buried here as many assume. His family ensured that his final resting place would be Cuautla, Morelos.

As we approached, I turned to Eduardo with a question. "Who do you think had a bigger impact on the Revolution—Zapata or Pancho Villa?"

Ever diplomatic, Eduardo smiled. "Both played vital roles in shaping the revolution, each in their own way." His answer was as balanced as it was thoughtful, leaving room for the complexities of Mexico's tumultuous past.

After concluding our history lesson, he asked, "Shall we eat a little something first?" It was both a question and a statement wrapped into one. As we entered the restaurant inside the Fronton, I noticed we were seated at a table for five. My math skills hadn't failed me yet—I figured other guests were joining us.

The first to arrive was Eduardo's first cousin on his father's side. He was around fifty, gregarious, fit, and impeccably mannered.

His command of English was far superior to mine, something I immediately admired. This gentleman, hailing from Mexico City, was a two-time world champion in Jai Alai—a feat that holds serious weight in any circle in the city. Soon after, the rest of our party arrived, greeted with enthusiastic hugs and hearty back-slapping. They were two of Eduardo's old friends, former Jai Alai players themselves, though their backs and knees, as they joked, weren't quite as robust as they used to be. We shared a moment of camaraderie over that, a universal truth.

We ordered a feast—tamales, enchiladas, tacos al pastor, and a couple of other dishes whose names have since slipped my mind. All of it was washed down with several bottles of Pacifico and Modelo Especial because, for certain things, you must go local.

The conversation flowed rapidly in Spanish, punctuated by slang and inside jokes that flew right over my head. Occasionally, someone would switch to English to check in with me. "Are you following along?" Eduardo asked. I smiled and assured him I had a firm grasp of the main themes. It's a slight stretch of the truth, I'll admit.

At one point, I deeply conversed with the Jai Alai champion, who graciously spoke in English for my benefit. Somehow, we drifted into the topic of bullfighting. With some enthusiasm, I recounted my experience watching the bullfights at Madrid's Plaza de Toros. I could see why the tradition evoked such deep cultural passion.

From across the table, José, one of Eduardo's friends, chimed in. "I used to be a rather well-known matador in Mexico City," he said casually. He explained that he had fought many battles in the ring in his youth, always respecting the bull as a formidable opponent. "The moment you lose respect for the bull," he added, his tone serious, "you can lose your life."

I couldn't help but think of Hemingway, who would have enjoyed discussing the traits of the Matador with Jose.

After a few more Modelo beers, Eduardo gave me a nudge with his bottle, nodding subtly toward Leon, seated a few spots away. Leon, I soon learned, had once been one of the most skilled gamblers in Mexico City. When our eyes met, he offered a half-shrug, only mildly self-conscious. As it turned out, Leon loved poker, often finding himself in high-stakes games at hidden poker rooms scattered throughout the city and in some of its most opulent casinos. José chimed in, recalling how those games would stretch long into the night, sometimes continuing well into the next day.

It was clear that I had fallen into some remarkable company. There was the twice Jai Alai world champion, as humble as he was accomplished; a former matador, who still carried himself with the quiet dignity of his dangerous profession; and, of course, Leon—the "retired" gambler who knew nearly every gambling den and poker room in Mexico City, along with its cast of celebrity players. And then there was Eduardo, whom I had known for several years. Coming from a well-established family with deep roots in the city, Eduardo was a passionate sportsman, an outstanding Jai Alai player, and an equally fierce competitor. Once a civil servant, he was now a successful businessman. I also couldn't forget that his family had built a Jai Alai court behind their house. I remembered watching him play there one afternoon, losing a few pesos in friendly bets.

Bets are placed, and the game is on!

We were seated just four rows from courtside, comfortably settled in with oversized cups of beer, ready to place a few bets. Eduardo nudged me, gesturing to the right. "Look over there," he said. Sure enough, it was the ex-presidential candidate from the PRI political party, accompanied by the former Mexico City mayoral candidate. Both had once been influential figures during President Enrique Peña Nieto's administration but had since fallen out of favor under the current leadership of President Andrés Manuel López Obrador. Such is the nature of politics—one's fortune can rise or fall with the whims of an administration. Eduardo, a mutual acquaintance, had ties to the old political heavyweights and the new president, Obrador. For him, it was all business and maintaining the right balance of alliances.

The sharp crack of the ball smashing into the front wall at over 100 mph signaled that the game had begun. Jai alai, famously promoted by the Basque government as "the fastest sport in the world," once held the world record for ball speed at

188 mph (302 km/h). That record was shattered in 2007 with an astonishing 204 mph (328 km/h). A word to the wise: even with a baseball catcher's mitt, it's best to steer clear of the ball's path. The atmosphere was electric, with a little betting here and there—well, maybe a lot of betting, as hawkers moved through the crowd. Men in sharp suits and women dressed as if for a night out dotted the audience, all eagerly placing bets. It certainly added to the excitement of the game.

We stayed through two thrilling matches featuring spectacular players, and by the end, Eduardo had collected his winnings. As we made our way out, there were more hugs, handshakes, introductions, and farewells. It was the perfect close to an unexpectedly fun Sunday afternoon.

I had been awake since 2 a.m. when my Uber finally arrived, and by then, I was exhausted and ready to sleep like the dead. My hotel was in the *La Reforma* district, a familiar part of town where I'd stayed on previous visits. This area hosts the city's main financial and business districts. The avenue is wide and elegantly laid out, with statues and monuments dotting the center. It's designed to evoke the grandeur of the Champs-Élysées and other famous Parisian boulevards.

My hotel differed from the typical high-end chain hotels catering to the tourist crowds. Fortunately, this meant I was less likely to bump into a Gringo, which, frankly, is worth its weight in gold. The further I can distance myself from the "Ugly American" stereotype, the better. The hotel leans more toward the traditional, almost old-world style. The staff are friendly, and I like to think they enjoy my attempts at speaking Spanish. I can manage most conversations, and, just like with French, I tend to speak quickly. It always keeps them guessing about my cultural roots until we have to dig deeper into the language.

Perhaps I'll have a Cognac with Miguel, my favorite bartender, in the cozy red velvet lounge. Maybe we can resume our earlier conversation on bullfighting. Tomorrow will be a long workday, but for now, a drink and some good discussion seem like the perfect end to this long day.

A Chilaquiles Breakfast on the Streets of Mexico City

*E*duardo and I set off on a leisurely morning walk toward his office, just a short distance from my hotel in the bustling *La Reforma* district. Even at this early hour, the streets of Mexico City were already springing to life. Pedestrians hurried along the sidewalks while buses, cars, and motorbikes weaved in and out of traffic, creating a vibrant urban scene. It was a lovely late fall morning, and the crisp air was refreshing, though I knew the temperature would climb to a pleasant 70 degrees by midday.

As we strolled, Eduardo guided me to his favorite street vendor. The vendor was busy ladling ingredients from a steaming pot into small Styrofoam containers, roughly the size of a McDonald's hamburger box, for a line of eager customers. A few stood nearby, already digging into their meals, and I had a feeling I'd soon find out what captivated them.

Eduardo took the opportunity to give me a quick history lesson on street vendors in Mexico City. "Over 75 percent of the population here eats from a street vendor at least once a week," he said, a statistic that lingered in my mind as I watched my order of chilaquiles take shape.

Street vending, Eduardo explained, has deep roots in Mexican culture, dating back to pre-Hispanic times. In today's Mexico City, more than 1.2 million people rely on street vending for their livelihoods, part of an informal sector that is as vital to the city's character as it is to its economy. These vendors make the streets lively and dynamic, offering affordable food and services that might otherwise be hard to find. From temporary stalls to bicycles outfitted for business, they sell everything from fresh fruit juices and tacos to essential repairs.

Their presence is ubiquitous—lining sidewalks, stationed outside metro stations, and clustered in parks. For many commuters who spend hours on public transportation, street vendors outside office buildings are often the only chance to grab a healthy, affordable breakfast. And today, I was about to experience this slice of Mexico City life firsthand.

The vendor expertly filled the bottom of the container with a thick, almost polenta-like mole mixture. I chose green salsa, which he generously layered before topping it off with a healthy dollop of crema fresca—Mexican fresh cream made from heavy cream and buttermilk. He added crumbled queso fresco, typically a blend of cow's and goat's milk, and slices of onion and creamy avocado to crown this creation. What an incredible symphony of flavors!

I stood at the corner with locals, spoon in hand, slowly digging from the bottom up, taking in the vibrant morning scene of Mexico City. Traffic buzzed, stylish commuters passed by, and Eduardo, my ever-entertaining companion, continued his stories. Occasionally, a driver would pull over, quickly order, and join our small group, savoring something delicious. A schoolgirl stopped by briefly, picked up a pineapple banana juice, and continued.

But a word of caution: the hearty and robust chilaquiles packed such flavor and substance that, despite my best efforts, I couldn't finish them all. I returned the remainder to the vendor with a satisfied sigh, anticipating my next encounter with Mexico City's dazzling flavors and experiences.

Consider this a public service announcement from someone who's been there before. If your tour of Mexico City includes arriving at a restaurant by bus with your travel companions, their passports, and any personal items dangling around their necks, only to find yourself at a spot serving bland, Mexican-American fare, prepare to be disappointed. I recommend asking your tour guide or bus driver to direct you to a place that offers authentic American cuisine and accepts U.S. dollars.

I apologize if this comes off as a rant, but encountering what feels like an "Ugly American" presence can be uncomfortable and even embarrassing. My experiences in Europe and Africa taught me to avoid drawing unnecessary attention abroad. If you're intent on making a scene, perhaps it's better to stick to the familiar comforts of home, like East Podunk's "Tastee Freez" and Budweiser.

I'll step down from my soapbox and return to my writing. This is just a friendly reminder to be mindful of how you represent yourself while traveling.

Seafood and Ambiance in Mexico City's Trendy Roma Norte

The restaurant where I found myself was again thanks to my customer Eduardo. We were in Roma Norte, the epicenter of Mexico City's culinary and artistic scene, just a stone's throw from Eduardo's home in La Condesa. With its blend of hipsters on bicycles and an influx of young professionals, this neighborhood exudes a unique charm. *Avenida Álvaro Obregón*, the area's leafy central avenue, is lined with a vibrant mix of eclectic eateries, lively sidewalk bars, and beautifully restored mansions. As a dedicated foodie, I was particularly drawn to Mercado Roma, where international food stalls meet a backdrop of colorful street art. It's a place where one can easily escape the hustle and bustle of downtown Mexico City.

After valet parking our car, we entered a stunning open-air restaurant renowned for its fresh seafood, all sourced directly from the Yucatan region and famed for its exceptional coastal offerings. The ambiance balanced between upscale sophistication—with its crisp table linens—and a bustling marketplace vibe. The clientele reflected this mix: locals winding down with beers and margaritas after work, a sprinkling of expats, and the occasional tourist thrown into the mix. Prices, though reasonable, were not my concern, if you catch my drift. It was a Monday, early evening—around 5 p.m.—so the crowd was more relaxed, not the multitudes you'd see on the weekends. We opted for a table near the sidewalk if I needed to vault over the railing to rescue someone. After a long, productive day at Eduardo's office, we were ready for a well-deserved, high-octane libation.

Barely had we settled in and glanced at the menu when the waiter arrived, serving us a shot glass of "Vuelve a la Vida," a spicy seafood cocktail. It was so flavorful that it commanded my immediate attention. As soon as we polished that off, the next round appeared: two classic Margaritas, perfectly timed to ease us into the evening. A brilliant touch! I half expected to be swept into a Mexican Hat Dance next, perhaps with a newfound chica. Eduardo, taking charge, ordered a few dishes to kick things off. I certainly wasn't about to stop him.

First on the table was a steaming bowl of *Mariscos*, a brothy Mexican seafood soup brimming with fish, shrimp, and other ocean treasures. I was captivated by the rich, comforting flavors of this dish. Yes, it was filling, but in such moments, you must be polite and do your best to finish what's served.

Next up was the *Ceviche Peruano*, seemingly swimming for their lives in an irresistible divine garlic sauce. "Two more Margaritas, por favor!" I nodded enthusiastically and polished off the remainder of my first one. We were having fun. Eduardo, as always, was an excellent and charming host. Whenever he visited me for business, I tried to return the favor as best I could. However, with limited restaurant options in my town, it was challenging. Eduardo often reminded me that we had already been to my chosen spot more than once.

The second round of Margaritas arrived in style, accompanied by a platter of Peruvian spicy chili clams. They were delicious and reminded me of the Spanish *almejas a la marinara*, though with a distinctly Mexican twist. We decided to split the red snapper—garlic Parmesan—encrusted—and it was prepared like nothing I'd tasted before. Crunchy on the outside yet moist and flavorful inside, it was perfection. Before long, two more Margaritas strolled onto our table and making themselves at home.

The service was friendly, though it could have been faster. Still, the seafood was incredible, and they assured us the place gets deafeningly loud on the weekends. But on this calm Monday night, the atmosphere was relaxed, and the waitstaff was eager to help us navigate the menu. It was the perfect spot to unwind, sip a few drinks with friends, and relax.

We took a breather and chatted about business—Eduardo's company, in particular. He was at a crossroads, contemplating either selling or expanding. These two different paths have vastly different implications. We sipped another Margarita to discuss his options before eventually tabling the conversation.

At one point, I asked Eduardo about city and neighborhood crime. He told me about a night he and three friends went to Roma Norte for dinner. They had just parked when two men, guns drawn, approached and demanded their wallets, watches, and the keys to their friend's Mercedes. It was a sobering reminder of how quickly things can change. While one can't live in constant fear, Eduardo stressed the importance of being smart, and sometimes, that means surrendering to the demands of an armed robber. It's better to live and fight another day.

La Terraza – Gran Hotel Ciudad de Mexico

*I*f you want to enjoy a few Mimosas on a warm Sunday morning, there's no better spot than La Terraza at the Gran Hotel Ciudad. The hotel is a magnificent landmark, well worth a few minutes of exploration, just like any savvy tourist would. Don't miss snapping a photo of the stunning stained-glass ceiling, and for a bit of adventure, take a ride in the charmingly old-fashioned elevator—though it wouldn't hurt to double-check your insurance first!

The real action happens on the fifth floor. With some luck, you'll score a table overlooking the Palace. The view from the restaurant is breathtaking, offering sweeping vistas of the Zócalo, the National Palace, and the Metropolitan Cathedral. It's a scene that's as unforgettable as the experience itself.

On my last day in Mexico City, I enjoyed a Sunday brunch with my customer Eduardo, who seems to have a knack for discovering all the city's hidden gems. He epitomizes a gracious host, ensuring every detail is perfect. As for the brunch itself, a couple of Mimosas in, I'd describe the food as decent but not extraordinary, with a bit of an assembly-line feel that didn't leave a lasting impression. However, the drinks, the view, and Eduardo's company made it a delightful Sunday."

Grilled Octopus Yucatan Style
Pulpo a la parrilla de Yucatán

For a business trip, this one was surprisingly pleasant. I found myself in the Mexican Caribbean, where the weather was warm and inviting, the views unforgettable, and the seafood simply divine.

As the day wound down, I felt the weight of fatigue—or perhaps outright exhaustion—after navigating a seemingly endless list of client demands. What I craved more than anything was rest, relaxation, and a good meal. On a solid recommendation, I went to a seafood restaurant fronting the beach, just off Boulevard Kukulcan.

A gentle offshore breeze made the evening remarkably comfortable. I sat by the shore, captivated by the dazzling white sand, so different from the coarse grains of our Mid-Atlantic beaches back home. The water was crystal clear, an almost hypnotic turquoise that stretched endlessly before me, drawing me in. It all felt dreamlike. As I gazed, my mind wandered to distant places—perhaps my secluded Gulf island or a brightly painted fishing boat gently rocking on these shimmering, turquoise waters.

A waiter in a crisp white uniform appeared at my side, quietly interrupting my pleasantly drifting thoughts — thanks to a few well-made Mojitos, I must admit — with a discreet *Señor?* I glanced up, and there he stood, balancing a large round tray, almost as big as he was, piled high with seafood. My confusion must have shown because he lowered the tray and, with polite precision, began to name each offering: snapper, mahi-mahi, tuna, grouper, octopus, sea bass, lobster, shrimp, prawns, and a few others that have since escaped me.

When I asked for his recommendation, he flashed a broad smile and pointed to the octopus. "Grilled," he said, *muy delicioso!* I trusted his expertise and ordered the octopus, along with another Mojito. There was still the matter of choosing an appetizer.

I went with a local favorite from the Yucatán: ceviche. Fresh raw fish marinated in citrus juices, its proteins thickened by the acidity, essentially "cooking" them. The dish was perfectly seasoned with tomatoes, onions, chilies, cilantro, salt, and coriander. It was an excellent choice, though the portion could have fed a small army. Still, I pressed on, and I know I'll order it again—guaranteed.

The main course arrived, and the grilled Yucatan-style octopus was a masterpiece. Its presentation begged to be admired before indulging, with the charred exterior glistening under the soft restaurant lighting. As I took my first bite, I was relieved to find it perfectly tender, not at all rubbery like an octopus can sometimes be. Each bite felt like a journey into something divine, and I savored it slowly, as though I had all the time in the world.

To close the meal, I treated myself to a rich Mexican flan, its creamy texture and delicate sweetness a fitting finale. It was the dessert that made you pause, appreciating the simple perfection. I was grateful I didn't have far to walk, especially after such a satisfying meal.

By the time I stepped outside, it was evening. The distant hum of music drifted through the streets, likely from a nearby bar or restaurant. A gentle breeze swept in, making the evening feel alive. It was the perfect night for a stroll back to my hotel.

PANAMA
ECHOES OF THE CANAL

Panama Bay

After thoughtful deliberation, I chose Panama City, Panama, as our next Latin American team meeting destination. This decision would be advantageous for our team. Hailing from Bogotá, Colombia, the flight was a relatively short journey, starkly contrasting to arduous long-hauls like Dubai, Delhi, or Beijing. The strategic location of Panama City, with its efficient airport and well-connected roads, was a key factor in this choice.

Tocumen International Airport greeted me with its modern, efficient design, a pleasant departure from the chaos I've encountered in other corners of the world. This was refreshingly smooth, unlike some less-than-fond memories where merely surviving the airport felt like an accomplishment. As I stepped onto Panamanian soil, Manuel's familiar face welcomed me, my trusted friend and business colleague, as I waited in the international arrivals hall.

The drive to downtown Panama was a quick and easy twenty-five miles on well-maintained roads. It's these little conveniences that one truly learns to appreciate with time. The skyline of Panama City, shimmering in the heat, resembled Miami, its sleek towers set against the vivid blue waters of the Gulf of Panama. It was a sight to behold.

I had carefully planned my trip to avoid Panama's rainy season, conscious of my unfortunate tendency to arrive in other places just in time for monsoon downpours as I had in Vietnam and India—those relentless rains, the flooding streets, and the oppressive humidity. In those moments, the only solace was in a dimly lit hotel bar, swapping travel miseries with fellow travelers. Fun times.

But here in Panama City, the weather was different—still hot and humid, but nothing I couldn't handle. It was almost pleasant—a stark contrast to those torrential experiences. This time, it felt like a walk in the park.

I was gathering our Latin American team for a two-day strategic planning and team-building event. This meant bringing together business owners and customers from Mexico, Costa Rica, Panama, Chile, Colombia, Peru, and Argentina. My usual approach was delegating on-the-ground logistics to the country representative; that role always went to Manuel for Panama. Manuel, a polished, well-educated businessman, ran a flourishing international export enterprise with his father. He would handle everything—from scouting suitable hotels to securing meeting spaces and, crucially, organizing a memorable group outing for the day after our meetings. I knew from experience that "all work and no play makes Juan a very dull boy."

True to form, Manuel secured our accommodations at the Hard Rock Hotel Panama, a 66-floor marvel that never fails to impress. The hotel's crown jewel is "BITS"—Bar in the Sky—an elegant rooftop bar and lounge perched on the 63rd floor, offering a breathtaking panorama of Panama Bay. For a dash of excitement, the elevator ride requires a switch at the 25th floor, a transition that adds a touch of suspense as you wait to ascend even higher. It reminded me of the Sheraton Hong Kong, its rooftop bar on the 118th floor, and its glass elevator that lets you soar above the city. The view from BITS, especially at night, is stunning—if you can keep your fear of heights in check and stop your legs from turning to jelly.

Since my last visit to Panama, the iconic Hard Rock Hotel has been rebranded as the Hard Rock Panama Megapolis, offering a refreshed and dynamic experience for travelers and locals. The revamped hotel remains in the heart of Panama City's bustling financial district, just a few blocks away from the now-infamous law firm Mossack Fonseca. This firm gained global notoriety for its central role in the "Panama Papers" scandal—a massive leak of 11.5 million confidential documents that pulled back the curtain on the shadowy financial dealings of the world's elite.

The documents exposed a labyrinth of offshore accounts, revealing personal secrets and dubious financial practices once carefully concealed. Among those named in the leak were over a dozen current or former world leaders, 128 public officials and politicians, and hundreds of celebrities, business moguls, and wealthy individuals. The adage, "Everything is legal as long as you don't get caught," seemed fitting for this case, which involved a staggering $1.36 billion—a figure likely to grow as more details emerge. It wasn't just the financial losses that stung; it was the brutal exposure of these individuals' financial misconduct under the harsh glare of public scrutiny.

On a more positive note, our annual planning session on the first day was a resounding success, reflected in the delighted reactions of our Latin business partners. The goal of this gathering was to bring together diverse business leaders with the shared objective of exporting their products to the U.S. Fluency in Spanish was essential for all attendees, ensuring smooth communication and collaboration. By the end of the day, country leaders were exchanging product ideas and sharing individual business strategies. The numerous photos taken throughout the event captured their genuine enjoyment and satisfaction with the process, making the session a highlight for everyone involved.

I paused for a moment to observe the dynamic interactions unfolding around me. On one side of the room, the representative from Chile was engaged in a deep conversation with our Costa Rican counterpart, tackling an export issue. Nearby, our Peru colleague explained the laboratory testing process's intricacies to the Argentine representative. At the same time, our Bogotá, Colombia representative captivated a potential client's attention with a focused sales pitch. The energy and discussions continued in this manner throughout the day.

Amidst it all, my good friend Manuel had a special surprise planned. We were all boarding a bus to visit one of Panama's most iconic landmarks—the Miraflores Lock at the Panama Canal.

Miraflores Lock

The Panama Canal, one of the Seven Wonders of the Modern World, is an absolute must-see for anyone visiting Panama. This impressive 82-kilometer (51-mile) artificial waterway is a testament to human innovation, cutting across the Isthmus of Panama and significantly reducing travel time for ships between the Pacific Ocean and the Caribbean Sea. As a vital artery for global maritime trade, the canal has facilitated the passage of over 900,000 vessels, underscoring its international significance and the importance of our visit.

Experiencing the Panama Canal in action, particularly at one of its locks, is awe-inspiring. If you find yourself at the Miraflores Visitors' Center when a massive ship navigates through, consider yourself fortunate. Watching a ship glide through the lock is a perfectly orchestrated engineering marvel, and the anticipation is well worth it. Having witnessed this spectacle twice, I would eagerly return for a third visit, continually impressed by the sheer magnitude and precision of the operation.

After departing from the canal, our trip continued to visit Panamá Viejo, the historic remnants of the original Panama City. Once the capital, this site was destroyed in 1671 by Welsh pirate Henry Morgan. Today, it offers a glimpse into Panama's past and lies in the suburbs of the modern capital.

We capped off our trip with an evening at the "Bar in the Sky." After snapping photos, sipping cocktails, and enjoying the ambiance, I exited early to avoid the inevitable elevator rush on the way down. Meanwhile, our energetic Latin American team stayed behind, dancing the night away and closing the bar.

Overall, the trip was unforgettable. It blended the awe-inspiring Panama Canal with the joy of hosting our Latin American business partners in a spectacular setting. Their presence elevated the experience, and I eagerly anticipate similar collaboration opportunities.

One final tip: Don't leave Panama without picking up an iconic Panama hat as a souvenir of your journey!

CHILE
CHASING THE CHILEAN HORIZON

View of the Andean mountain range from a small
airfield on the outskirts of Santiago

The flight from Washington, D.C. to Santiago took 11 hours and 15 minutes—a far cry from a quick cross-border hop by any stretch of the imagination. This was my second visit to Chile, though the first was brief and confined to the capital, Santiago. We attended a trade show filled with back-to-back technical presentations on that trip. It reminded me of my time in Beijing, sitting through sessions conducted in Mandarin while preparing to present our own. You don't take notes during these presentations but consume copious amounts of tea.

Perhaps the extraordinary cuisine was the most memorable aspect of my visit to Santiago. As a self-proclaimed foodie, I've developed a discerning palate and a keen eye for quality. I don't casually use the word "excellent" when it comes to food—if it doesn't meet a certain standard, I'm not one to shy away from saying so. Calling balls and strikes can be a rather brutal affair in the culinary world.

One of our new distributors, who fortunately had a refined taste for both food and wine, chose the restaurant. We began with *paila marina*, a traditional Chilean seafood soup or light stew, elegantly served in an earthenware bowl, as is customary. It boasted a rich shellfish stock brimming with fresh varieties of shellfish and fish, harmonized with the warmth of paprika, parsley, and other local spices. My Chilean guide was instrumental in helping me appreciate the subtleties of this dish.

For the main course, the *catch of the day*—Chilean sea bass—was sublime. It was a revelation paired with a Sauvignon Blanc from Chile's renowned Central Valley. The wine was crisp, earthy, and ideally suited to my preferences. The vineyards of that region are indeed a gift to the world.

And with that, it was "just an OK meal"—though, I jest, of course. It was an unforgettable experience.

This, my second trip to Chile, began at Santiago Airport, where I was met by a driver arranged by Mateo, my new distributor. The driver informed me that I would be meeting Mateo for an early dinner at a restaurant near his home in San Antonio, a coastal port city and the capital of the San Antonio Province in the Valparaíso Region.

Meeting Mateo for dinner would be a unique experience, not only because we were gathering in his hometown rather than Santiago's bustling capital but also because I would meet his family. As we drove through the picturesque Chilean countryside, I felt a growing connection with Mateo and his roots, appreciating the contrast between this serene landscape and the intense business negotiations that had brought us together.

The one-hour drive from Santiago to San Antonio gave me time to reflect on the circumstances that led to our partnership. Searching for a distributor to represent our firm in Chile's competitive market, I contacted Mateo through social media. After a few exchanges, we agreed to meet at a time that suited us both. I mentioned that I'd be in La Paz, Bolivia, the following week, and while it wasn't exactly next door, I invited him to meet me there for a face-to-face conversation.

To my surprise, the day after I arrived in La Paz, I found Mateo waiting downstairs, ready to discuss his proposal. Despite the challenges of adjusting to La Paz's high altitude—13,000 feet above sea level—Mateo's confidence shone through as he pitched a plan that sounded quite promising. Soon after my return to the U.S., we formalized our partnership. That trip to La Paz had its fair share of memorable moments, but those stories will have to wait for another time.

We arrived to a warm round of welcomes, and it wasn't long before I was faced with a difficult choice—hunger or thirst. We cracked open a few local Cerveza Cristal beers, letting their crispness refresh us as we studied the menu with growing anticipation. On Mateo's recommendation, a plate of golden empanadas quickly approached the table, each filled with savory beef, melted cheese, or tender seafood. These were soon followed by a seafood sampler that boasted the freshest tastes of the coast. Naturally, I couldn't resist the ceviche—my weakness—and it didn't disappoint bright, tangy, and as fresh as the sea breeze.

Determined not to hold back, I dove into the *Chorrillana* for my main course—a decadent, indulgent dish of crispy French fries piled high with succulent beef, sausages, sautéed onions, and fried eggs—certainly a heart-healthy option if you believe in living dangerously. I fought my way through it, though I'm not ready to admit my eyes may have been bigger than my stomach.

By the end of the meal, I could almost hear my bed beckoning me from afar, but before heading back, I took a moment to step outside. The coastline stretched before me, bathed in the glow of the setting sun. The calm sea air brushed my face, and the rhythmic roar of the waves filled my ears. I found myself utterly mesmerized by the sight, sound, and smells. I could have stood there for hours; the scene was captivating and simple.

Into the Wild Blue Yonder

The next day, Mateo invited me on a small tour on his plane. Strapped into the front seat of the 4-seater Piper Cub, the engine humming, Mateo meticulously went through the pre-flight checklist, including a review of the plane's performance data and emergency checklist and a few pages more of checklist items.

Departure time

The anticipation was palpable for me, punctuated by an occasional burst of Spanish instructions from the little control tower crackling over the radio. For all I knew, they could have been saying, "Once over the Pacific, eject the gringo." The moment was charged with adventure and, yes, a hint of uncertainty, but I was eager to soar up into the wild blue yonder.

As we taxied slowly to the end of the runway, we turned, and Mateo revved the engines. The chatter from the control tower continued. Soon, we were poised for takeoff. Moments later, the ground dropped away beneath me as Mateo banked westward, revealing in the distance the breathtaking Chilean coastline stretching as far as the eye could see.

Then, to my delight, to my right, the San Alfonso Del Mar Resort came into view — home to the world's largest swimming pool. I had read about it and was eager to witness for myself its enormity. The sight took my breath away; this was no ordinary swimming pool, not the size of any backyard pool we may have been accustomed to. It spanned over nine football fields, holding sixty-six million gallons of water within its 20-acre expanse. The pool's construction had cost billions of dollars. Its sheer scale and beauty left me stunned. This was no mere lap pool; swimming from end to end could have been a lifelong endeavor. As a matter of record, I should add that Citystars *Sharm El Sheikh* claims to be the world's largest swimming pool at the southern tip of Egypt's Sinai Peninsula, overlooking the Gulf of Aqaba. Who will dispute a few thousand square meters, more or less?

We banked gently over the Pacific, the aircraft steadily climbing as we turned eastward. Soon, we were swallowed by a blanket of vast, billowing clouds, soft and inviting, like floating tufts of cotton. The surreal sight made it seem as though you could reach out and scoop a handful. As we ascended through the cloud layer, the sky above broke open into a brilliant expanse of blue, illuminated by the bright sun. Far on the horizon, the majestic Andes

Mountains came into view, their snow-capped peaks gleaming against the skyline. The sight took my breath away—a reminder of nature's grandeur. Stretching over 7,000 kilometers (4,300 miles) along the western coast of South America, the Andes are one of the most extended mountain ranges in the world, cutting through Argentina, Bolivia, Chile, Colombia, Ecuador, Peru, and Venezuela.

No in-flight movies

Just beyond Santiago, Mateo began our descent. I scanned the landscape expecting to see a large, modern airfield like Dulles International. Instead, Mateo pointed ahead. Surprisingly, I only saw a narrow strip of dirt masquerading as a landing zone. Half-jokingly, I asked if we were making a drug pickup or perhaps a delivery. The strip looked like something out of a covert operation—a place where either a cartel kingpin or a U.S. government agent might emerge. My mind raced through wild scenarios, but we soon touched down smoothly on what could only generously be called an "airfield."

As we taxied to a halt, I realized pilots like Mateo must be familiar with all kinds of landing strips, from the grandest international airports to these small, out-of-the-way spots. Mateo mentioned he frequently flies into Santiago for business and family trips. I unbuckled my seatbelt, only to discover, to my horror, that my door hadn't fully latched. It swung open with a casual nudge, and I made a mental note to triple-check next time—unless I fancied a deep dive over the Andes without a parachute. It's always the small things that can turn an otherwise perfect outing into a nightmare.

At the edge of the strip, a car and driver waited for us. Mateo turned to me with a grin, informing me we were headed to a winery. "Don't worry," he said with a wink, "I'll stick to water." I, on the other hand, had no such intention.

Colchagua-based winery Montes

The Colchagua Valley, nestled in the heart of Chile's central wine region, is one of the country's most renowned valleys, celebrated as an icon of Chilean wine production. Our destination, Montes Wines, was founded here in 1987, in this valley of sweet dreams.

Montes is an impressive operation with several remarkable features. The winery building was designed according to Feng Shui principles, blending architecture and energy flow seamlessly with the landscape. The company produces a wide range of wines from Chile's classic grape varieties, including Cabernet Sauvignon, Carmenère, Merlot, Syrah, and Chardonnay. Among their standout wines is *Purple Angel*, an iconic Carmenère-predominant blend, which serves as the flagship wine of Montes and is one of Chile's most renowned labels.

A highlight of the winery is the unique, semi-circular underground cellar at the heart of the building. Here, 800 new French oak barrels are carefully lined up, awaiting their role in shaping the next chapter of Montes' winemaking story. The barrels rest in a serene ambiance, accompanied by the soft sound of Gregorian chants—a truly striking and unusual experience that leaves an indelible impression.

After our visit, we drove back to the small, dusty airfield. Mateo methodically went through his pre-flight checklist while I made sure my door was securely closed—my entire contribution to pre-flight preparations. By late afternoon, we touched down at the modest airport. Soon after, I was welcomed into the office of the club president, who, in a hospitable gesture, pulled out a bottle of Scotch from his desk. We toasted, though whether to someone or something was unclear. His hesitant English and my shaky Spanish made our conversation a rich, albeit unconventional, exchange.

A few "snorts" later, we departed for my hotel. What a day.

LIMA
THE CITY OF KINGS

*L*ima, the capital of Peru, often referred to as the "City of Kings" (Ciudad de los Reyes), is uniquely situated on a desert strip between the Pacific Ocean and the towering Andes Mountains. The city boasts a beautifully preserved colonial center and houses several remarkable collections of pre-Columbian art. The name "Peru" is derived from a Quechua word meaning "land of abundance," reflecting the immense economic wealth generated by the Inca civilization, which ruled the region for centuries. The depth of Peru's cultural history is rich and profoundly impressive, leaving a lasting impression on me.

My journey to Lima was not a daunting, lengthy ordeal from a far-off land. Instead, it was a smooth and convenient 9-hour, 30-minute flight from Dulles International Airport to Jorge Chávez International Airport. The ease of travel only heightened my anticipation for the adventures that awaited me in Lima.

The historic center of Lima, a UNESCO World Heritage Site, is a captivating blend of culture, history, and architecture. Its designation as a heritage site reminds visitors to resist the temptation to bring home a piece of its cultural treasures. Violating these protections could lead to serious consequences (though being "escorted" to Machu Picchu for a blindfolded walk along the Stairway of Death might sound more dramatic than accurate!).

Lima was founded in 1535 by the Spanish conquistador Francisco Pizarro, and its historic center is aptly named the "Ciudad de los Reyes" (City of Kings). The strong Spanish influence on the city's architecture and culture is no surprise—Lima was established as the capital of the Spanish territories in the Americas, effectively marking the fall of the Inca Empire, the largest pre-Columbian civilization. Spanish colonial rule over Peru lasted until the country declared its independence in 1821, although full independence wasn't secured until 1824—a rich chapter in Peru's noble history.

Now, on to the food! Lima's culinary scene is, without question, superb. The city's cuisine is a delightful fusion of indigenous, African, and Asian (especially Chinese) influences, resulting in a gastronomic paradise. Signature seafood dishes like ceviche and tiradito are must-tries, showcasing the bounty of the Pacific coast with vibrant, fresh flavors. Lima is a mecca for food lovers, and those passionate about exceptional cuisine will go to great lengths to savor its offerings. With its diverse influences and deep-rooted traditions, Lima's culinary landscape is as complex and fascinating as its history—a subject I could explore enthusiastically.

The business meetings went smoothly, and meeting and greeting their corporate team in person was a pleasure. Putting a face to a name works wonders in easing future challenges. Communication is vital when conducting business across borders. Whether crafting a letter in English, Spanish, or French, there's an undeniable art to getting the tone and nuances right—just as when composing correspondence for customers in Asia.

Years ago, I was recruiting for an international attorney specializing in European chemical regulations. I approached a French firm with a letter written in English. To put it mildly, the partner's response was less than agreeable. I responded with a letter in French, and the tone of their reply transformed utterly. It was elegant and gracious and ended with an invitation to visit their offices the next time I was in Brussels or Paris. This experience was a reminder that understanding customs, procedures, and communication is essential in international business.

Costa Verde is one of Lima's many surfing spots on the Pacific Ocean. A little-known factoid for those who might recall The Beach Boys' song "Surfin' Safari" is that Cerro Azul beach, which they mention, is in Peru, about an hour south of Lima

While working with one of our distributors, they treated me to a tour of the Pacific Coast. The view was stunning, and for a brief moment, I felt as though I was back at Huntington Beach, with my toes in the sand, the waves crashing along the Southern California shoreline. Surfers dotted the waters, and it was a breathtaking sight to behold. We parked and headed to the beach to watch the surfing up close. Unlike the sandy beaches I'm used to, particularly those on the Atlantic side, this beach was rocky—reminiscent of the pebbly, rugged shores of Southern France, which make it difficult to walk or even relax on.

We stopped at an authentic Peruvian restaurant, though the décor leaned heavily toward a Spanish theme. The menu was a thrilling exploration of Peruvian classics, offering an array of dishes from hearty soups to flavorful entrées and everything in between. Without hesitation, we ordered Pisco Sours—the signature Peruvian cocktail—for the table. Then came the appetizers, which my host deemed essential. Among them was an intriguing plate of raw fish, delicately garnished with pickled vegetables.

Having traveled through countries like China, Turkey, Vietnam, India, and more, I'm no stranger to culinary adventures. I've learned that while such experiences can be a gamble, the real gamble sometimes comes the next day. It's that unsettling feeling as if something inside you has curled up and died, and at that moment, you'd almost prefer to join it. Trust me, I speak from experience.

Following the recommendation of my culinary advisor, I opted for *Tacu Tacu a lo Pobre*, a delightful Peruvian dish that exceeded my expectations. This rustic country-fried steak, served with a sunny-side-up egg atop a bed of beans and rice, was elevated by a sweet and sour tomato sauce and complemented by a fried banana. The satisfying crunch of the steak, paired with the well-seasoned beans and rice, made for a profoundly fulfilling meal. By the end, I felt like I had completed a culinary workout and was a strong candidate for a well-deserved nap!

Please help yourself by eating a variety of Peruvian seafood appetizers
and the ever-present Pisco Sour, the national drink if there is one

On my final day, I found my suitcase slightly heavier than when I had arrived. I was bringing home a beautiful coffee table book on Peru and a bottle of Pisco. With one bottle of Pisco still waiting for me at home from a previous trip, the time is approaching to mix up a fresh batch of Pisco Sours! (The recipe can be found in the book appendix.)

A farewell luncheon was graciously hosted in my honor, with the company's senior leadership team in attendance. While I typically engage with the CEO and his marketing and sales staff, I welcomed the opportunity to meet other key members of the organization. The luncheon occurred at *El Mirador*, a restaurant on a peninsula near the Naval Academy of Peru (Escuela Naval del Perú), offering stunning views of the beach and the vast Pacific Ocean.

Ceviche and more

We had an extraordinary luncheon visitor. Each year, the warm Pacific waters along Peru's northern coastline are transformed into a wondrous spectacle of majestic humpback whales breaching the surface in graceful leaps. Unfortunately, I was a bit slow on the draw and only captured a parting glimpse of the magnificent creatures.

All I saw was a glimpse of a mighty tail

And a fleeting image of a humpback

After a final round of Pisco Sours, it was fond farewells to everyone; my visit was over. In a short while, I would be on my way home.

On my flight home, I had the opportunity to reflect on the tremendous value of personal interactions with international customers. Face-to-face meetings foster connections and provide insights that can't be replicated through phone calls, emails, or other digital communications. While a quick Zoom call or feedback from a sales team can be helpful, they often lack the depth and immediacy that comes with an in-person visit. Meeting clients in person allows for a comprehensive understanding of their challenges and preferences, offering a clearer perspective on how they use your products or services while strengthening the professional bond.

For instance, sharing a meal with a customer and their family in Hyderabad, India, or enjoying lunch with a client in Beirut establishes connections that virtual meetings cannot match. These face-to-face interactions yield real-time feedback, enhance customer satisfaction, and foster long-term loyalty. Most importantly, they make customers feel genuinely valued—an appreciation often translates into significant, tangible rewards.

Two of my customers illustrate this point well. A client from Panama shared, "In seven years of working with Richard, he has demonstrated a profound understanding of the global market, offering practical strategies that have led to major improvements for his international team and impressive short-term results." Another client from Costa Rica noted, "Richard has been instrumental in our company's growth, helping us build alliances across Latin America. He is a visionary and a great motivator, always supporting us throughout the years."

These testimonials underscore the importance of meaningful personal interactions in nurturing professional relationships and achieving long-term success. In-person visits elevate customer satisfaction and reinforce your brand's value, ensuring lasting partnerships built on trust and understanding.

BRAZIL
RUA AUGUSTA: HEARTBEAT OF SÃO PAULO

The Octávio Frias de Oliveira Bridge (Rafael Paulucci |Getty Images)

*A*fter a ten-hour flight from Dulles International Airport, I eagerly landed at São Paulo-Guarulhos International Airport. The primary purpose of my return was to finalize a crucial deal with a new customer I'd been pursuing since my last visit. Alongside this critical meeting, I had two other key appointments that required traveling well beyond São Paulo's city limits. Given the city's notorious traffic, I prepared for a two-hour journey each way.

São Paulo, the largest city in Brazil and one of the largest in the world, is a vibrant, dynamic metropolis renowned for its cultural diversity, economic significance, and fast-paced lifestyle. The city's fabric has been deeply shaped by a rich immigration, particularly from countries like Italy, Japan, Lebanon, and Germany. The influence of these communities is not just a historical footnote but a living, breathing part of São Paulo's modern identity, seen in its neighborhoods, cuisine, festivals, and daily life.

Italian immigration to Brazil began in 1875, with a significant wave between 1888 and 1902, during which approximately 900,000 Italians settled there. São Paulo, with its booming coffee plantations, became a prime destination for these immigrants, who were particularly valued for their Latin roots and shared Catholic faith. This influx has left a lasting Italian imprint on São Paulo, which remains evident today in its culture, architecture, and culinary scene.

The Italian influence in São Paulo is not merely a historical footnote; it's a vibrant, integral part of the city's cultural fabric, evident in its community, cuisine, and even language. This influence becomes immediately apparent for newcomers, infusing daily life with a unique blend of Italian-Brazilian charm.

Nightlife and Gastronomy

São Paulo's nightlife is legendary, with Rua Augusta at its core—a bustling hub filled with bars, clubs, and live music venues that pulse with energy late into the night. While the atmosphere is intoxicating, it's important to stay vigilant, as pickpockets can be an issue in such busy areas. Rua Augusta is alive with fast talkers and enticing promises, where pubs and clubs vie for attention, each offering its slice of São Paulo's vibrant nightlife.

Beyond its nightlife, São Paulo's culinary scene is equally renowned. The city offers a dizzying array of dining options, from local street food to sophisticated high-end restaurants. Whether you're craving traditional Brazilian fare, international flavors, or innovative fusion dishes, São Paulo is a gastronomic paradise that promises travelers an unforgettable culinary journey.

Just a short walk from my hotel and slightly off the main drag of Rua Augusta, I stumbled upon a street that was home to four Italian restaurants. These ranged from casual pizzerias to family-style eateries and even upscale dining establishments—an unexpected delight in the heart of São Paulo. I chose the family-style restaurant, and the moment I stepped inside, it felt like I had been transported to a rustic trattoria deep in the Italian countryside. The ambiance was authentically Italian, with waitstaff in traditional black smocks, children playing underfoot, and couples savoring wine by candlelight. The only reminder that I was still in Brazil was the sound of Brazilian Portuguese filling the room.

I settled on Osso Buco, one of my favorite Italian dishes for dinner. A Milanese classic, Osso Buco features tender braised veal shanks simmered in a rich wine and vegetable sauce, finished with a vibrant gremolata made of parsley, lemon zest, and garlic. A reasonably priced bottle of Chianti perfectly complemented this exquisite meal. The evening was made even more charming by the linguistic dance that ensued. The waiter mainly spoke Portuguese, peppered with a few English words. I relied on a mix of my limited

Portuguese and Spanish, with occasional help from my fluency in French. The interplay of languages added a delightful layer to the experience, reminding me of when I once recruited a Russian attorney for a prestigious U.S. law firm in Moscow. Partway through our discussions, the attorney paused to ask if I would mind switching from English to French. I, of course, agreed, and the interview progressed—an example of the imperative of having more than one language in one's arsenal when conducting business.

Somehow, despite the language barriers, it all worked out beautifully, making the experience all the more memorable.

A delicious Osso Buco - A classic Italian dish

A Hidden Gem Tucked Away in Sao Paulo, Brazil

The Ca'd'Oro Hotel, or simply the Cadoro as I affectionately call it, is nestled in the Consolação district at the heart of São Paulo. The hotel is located on Rua Augusta 129 and boasts a prime location—truly "close to everything." The name "Ca'd'Oro" is derived from a historic palace on Venice's Grand Canal, once used to host distinguished guests visiting the city.

This hotel is the modern reincarnation of the Grand Cadoro, which was sadly torn down in the early 1990s. The original hotel was renowned for its distinguished clientele, including Brazil's political and military elite, who frequented its elegant dining rooms to sip champagne, discuss politics, and mingle over business and pleasure. Today's Cadoro still carries the essence of that golden era, effortlessly transporting its guests back to a time when civility, impeccable service, and world-class gastronomy were guaranteed. There's a distinct sense of nostalgia in its air, a charm I find irresistibly appealing. Perhaps my age makes me long for these relics of old-world elegance, but I don't mind. The European ambiance here has always drawn me in.

The original Cadoro owners were pioneers in introducing Northern Italian cuisine to Brazil. Their influence brought dishes that São Paulo had never seen before—game meats like partridge, quail, pheasant, rabbit, and duck paired with delicate pasta and creamy polentas. Piedmontese *bollito misto*, Ossobuco di Vitello, and Carpaccio were just some gastronomic treasures that found their way into the city's culinary landscape thanks to this hotel.

Now, nearly a year after my first visit to São Paulo, I find myself returning to the Cadoro Hotel—there was never any doubt about where I would stay. Upon arrival, the staff at the check-in counter politely inquired if I had been a guest before, as I seemed familiar. The aging bellboy greeted me with a broad smile, clearly remembering me from my stay last year. It felt good to be back. Once in my room, I stepped onto the small balcony, its waist-high guardrail offering a dizzying view from twenty stories up. Below me, São Paulo's vast urban landscape unfolded in all directions, its endless sprawl stretching toward the horizon like an ocean of concrete and steel. The city felt infinite.

My morning view of São Paulo

I contemplated a critical decision: whether to indulge in the elegance of the Cadoro's dining room. With only three nights in São Paulo and a demanding business schedule ahead, I knew I had to make every moment count. Despite the miles I still had to travel to reach my clients in São Paulo State, I promised myself I would savor every culinary adventure the city had. It was a promise I intended to keep.

What things do I love about this Cadoro restaurant? It's easy. I would start with the wait staff, who were all great. I enjoyed working through the few words of *Portunhol* (a fusion of

Portuguese and Spanish spoken in border countries like Uruguay and Paraguay). The wait staff equally enjoyed correcting my use of a Spanish word with the correct Portuguese one. It was a true culinary and linguistic adventure! I had a similar brief discussion with a hotel employee in Lisbon who felt it necessary to correct my version of a greeting, reminding me that I was in Portugal, not in Catalonia, Spain—duly noted!

I loved starting my lunches at the hotel restaurant with a basket of fresh artisan bread, rolls, butter, and an olive oil mixture to beat the band. What looked like miniature red cocktail onions in olive oil had a delicious tangy taste. I had my share of these on a visit to the Mercado Municipal, where I found a stand with a carton packed on display, and the owner kindly offered me samples.

The ravioli with brie cheese filling and fresh tomato sauce with Sicilian lemon flavor were to die for. A simple salad will do—elegant and simple. Thank you! It was an excellent lunch that I enjoyed immensely.

A quick note about my last evening and my exquisite dinner: the dinner menu was a rabbit dish with *Fazzoletti* Pasta (large pasta squares) smothered in a delicious brown sauce! It was a lovely combination, and I felt like I had been transported deep into the Italian countryside. All I needed were my tweeds and a hunting gun. It was a dish that, in many ways, was also very reminiscent of my days as a youth at our house in the Brittany countryside. Our housekeeper, cook, and beautiful person would walk out the kitchen door holding a well-used, razor-sharp kitchen knife in one hand and a poor rabbit in the other. I can clearly say that the rabbit was not offered a last cigarette. Our cook would have me hold the lifeless creature until we returned to the kitchen.

This rabbit dish with *Fazzoletti* was succulent, and the rich sauce mixed with the pasta was heavenly.

Just as I finished, Fabricio, the hotel's third-generation owner, young, energetic, and smartly dressed in a grey sharkskin suit, shirt open, stopped by my table to inquire if I was satisfied with dinner. I told him it had been a long, long time since I tasted rabbit this delicious. Almost in a conspiratorial whisper, he told me that the table next to me was tasting something new to the menu, a brie infused with truffles. Would I like some? I politely begged off but made a mental note for next time.

What other way to cap off a great meal? I skipped the delicious-looking desserts and went for a cappuccino. The coffee came with white chocolates, cookies, and grapes steeped in Grappa for your tasting enjoyment—almost desert. After dinner, I enjoyed having a Guatemalan (in the absence of any *Diplomatico*, my go-to from Venezuela) sipping rum to cap things off. It's the little things that count. A Cubano Montecristo cigar would have been most welcomed.

As I nursed my rum, I reflected on the past few days in São Paulo and the progress made. The new customer was now part of my team, and I looked forward to helping his small company grow, all while strengthening our brand in Brazil, where the commercial landscape presents no small challenge. The value of meeting customers face-to-face remains undeniable. Whether it's a two-hour drive to meet a potential client or hosting a special lunch at the hotel for my new customer and his senior staff, I understand that relationship building across continents is both possible and demanding. I remained optimistic, though fully aware of the work still ahead.

LA PAZ
The City That Touches
the Clouds

If you want to feel as if the sky is within your reach, then La Paz, Bolivia,

one of the highest cities in the world, has to be your next stop...

La Paz Airport: A Bolivian welcome

I was on an Avianca puddle jumper from Lima to La Paz, eagerly anticipating my arrival despite the hectic schedule that awaited me. With inconvenient departure times, I knew I wouldn't be landing until just past 11 PM. We touched down at La Paz International Airport—also known as Manuel Márquez de León International Airport—and as soon as we exited the plane, we were herded into lines by customs officials. The selection process began immediately: those with proper visas were to the right, and everyone else was to the left.

The visa fee was $600, cash only, of course, and inability to pay meant being sent back to your point of origin. I was caught off guard despite researching the visa requirements online—I didn't have one. I missed something, and now I had to think on my feet—to improvise, in other words.

I never make it a habit to carry that amount of cash, especially when traveling internationally. It looks too inviting if stopped by the police, but this time, I was out of luck, and no hard cash equaled no visa. The math was simple. Barring a miracle, I was about to be turned away, put on the next flight, and returned to Lima. "Thank you very much; you have a lovely country here," I thought sarcastically.

But then, an ever-helpful bureaucracy informed me not to worry: "Señor, there are ATMs in the main hall for your convenience. (read, we want your cash.) Please hand me your passport to ensure your safe return." Nothing is quite as disconcerting as handing over your passport, especially to a rather shabby-looking stranger in military fatigues. I wanted to ask if he had just returned from Cuba. I did not.

I passed through a line of curious onlookers, flanked by a few airport police in mirrored sunglasses, in the event of a revolution. I was wondering if I was heading to a firing squad. The whole scenario felt like a dystopian nightmare, something straight out of a black-and-white film titled "Death in La Paz," with yours truly in the starring role running from someone. I half-expected to be stopped after crossing the international line, then asked for my passport, and subsequently accused of entering the country illegally—a trick our friends in Russia and China have perfected with chilling efficiency.

I'll admit I was getting a bit stressed out. It happens sometimes, especially when surrounded by so many men in camo outfits and holding well-oiled machine guns. Call me silly that way.

I bolted out of the gate, focused on my mission. My first stop—*"No, la macchina no fonctiona."* I got it, the damn machine's busted. I hurried through the deserted terminal, rows of airline kiosks standing empty, waiting. Not a human face to be found. Finally, I spotted an ATM almost hidden from view. I used my corporate card, but it was promptly rejected. Well, that's comforting. With a quiet prayer, I tried my card. Thankfully, the ATM accepted it, spitting out the necessary bills, one after another.

La Paz International Airport sits at an astounding 13,000 feet above sea level. The city, the world's highest administrative capital, perches on the Andes' Altiplano plateau, more than 12,000 feet up. At this altitude, the air holds just 60% of the oxygen found at sea level, causing interesting effects on the human body— headaches, nausea, dizziness, and disorientation, to name a few. What more could someone ask for?

With cash in hand, feeling noticeably lightheaded and short of breath from sprinting around the airport hall, I returned to the front lines of bureaucracy. The same bored onlookers still lingered, the sleepy guards stood around, and the lone customs official now sat behind a small desk, neatly arranging his cash. I bought back my passport for $600. The official stamped it with a flourish and a broad smile, informing me that my visa was "good for one year!" I felt like telling him to take the cash, knock himself out, and buy one of his wives a cheap used car. I was getting irritable and tired. But what little sense I had remaining told me to pick up my suitcase and walk away.

By this time, after 2 A.M., La Paz International Airport had turned into a ghost town. Would my driver be patiently waiting for me as promised? Only If I believed in fairy tales. Yet, a lone cab magically pulled up, and I jumped in, not even thinking where he might decide to take me or dispose of me, perhaps in little pieces scattered along the airport road. I recall hearing that such a timely occurrence was probably not the hallmark of an official cab despite some city slogan painted on the doors. Clever kidnappers in Bolivia and elsewhere, I am sure, sometimes impersonate police officers (or even a cab driver to target foreigners. They use fake police ID cards, uniforms, and even police stations to fool victims. In the dead of night, no one would come looking for me. I knew I was risking it.

As you circle down from the airport to the capital, you gradually drop about a thousand feet in altitude. It was an out-of-body experience—a bad movie, perhaps, with subtitles or something worthy of a Hitchcock movie. Disoriented and out of breath, in a car held together with baling wire and no seatbelts, circling down the hill, tires screeching as my driver, with his perpetual smile, seemingly unphased, navigated each sharp turn with ease. The last time I had a cab driver from Hell was after a luncheon with my customer and his extended family at a beautiful and secluded location in the *Chouf* mountains high above Beirut. By the time I left, it was evening. Driving down the hill towards Beirut, my young driver had one hand on the wheel while holding an iPhone in the other and playing some game. He would keep his arm out the window, every so often, for better reception, and occasionally, even lean out the window to get a better screen view. With each sharp turn down the mountain, it was not whether I would die but when and how. Having cheated death this far, I told the driver, in no uncertain terms, enough with the game and put both hands on the wheel, please. Or there was one time when I had this cabbie driving me to North Delhi through incredible traffic and a restive crowd, but that's another story.

La Paz by dead of night

Late night La Paz, the World's Highest Capital, is an experience, teetering on the edge of the surreal. It had that familiar aura reminiscent of many cities I have visited for business in various parts of the developing world. That unmistakable ghostly, yellowish light seeping out from the street lamps, casting an eerie glow over everything. Narrow cobbled side streets with chaotic masses of telephone and other electronic wire overhead. Homes, glued next to each other, painted in various colors: green, red, blue, and yellow. Shutters closed tight as a drum. Many buildings appear ramshackle by day, but they seem even more dilapidated under darkness, often little more than unfinished concrete structures standing as silent sentinels. A police car was stationed on a corner, waiting for something. The city feels almost abandoned—no stray dogs, no elusive black cat, nothing. A lone elderly man, in a traditional Bolivian bowler hat, stood just under a street light. No agenda, timeless moments. La Paz was asleep, and I had no intention of discovering anything beyond that.

My driver turned down yet another narrow side street, finally stopping, and turned to me with a big grin, mumbling about something he seemed amusing. He slammed his taxi into gear and left in a cloud of blue smoke. I expected to see some signs of civilization, perhaps a neon "Hotel" sign. I double-checked my itinerary; this was my hotel, though no lights were visible and no smiling doorman was ready to open the door. With my suitcase in hand, I did the only polite thing I could think of: I banged hard on the front door several times and waited. Eventually, the front door curtains parted ever so slightly, and a pair of eyes peered out, suspiciously scrutinizing me before opening the door. It felt as if maybe I'd stumbled into the Hotel California.

At the check-in, the bleary-eyed man I'd woken up handed me a white envelope, which I saw was from Felix, my customer. Inside was a welcome note and a reminder that he'd pick me up at 8 A.M.—this morning. Also in the envelope were two white pills. Felix strongly recommended that I take an altitude sickness tablet before bed. The thought of ingesting unidentified "white pills" in La Paz or anywhere on the continent didn't sit well with me. I might consider trying coca tea readily available in supermarkets, restaurants, and cafés, or, if I felt adventurous, chew some coca leaves and embrace the altitude, perhaps even touch the sky.

Once in my room, I turned on the television and caught the only thing: a soccer match. I scrounged for some snacks and downed two whiskeys from the minibar. I called it a night, hoping to catch a few hours of sleep.

Our man in La Paz

Morning arrived sooner than expected. The front desk called to inform me that my visitor had arrived. It took a moment, but I remembered my interview with Mateo that I had arranged. I had been searching for a potential new candidate to run the Chilean market. Mateo's eagerness to meet was commendable and precisely what I sought. I was still feeling the effects of the altitude—dizziness and shortness of breath would be with me for a while. Perhaps that little white pill would have been a wise choice after all. I decided to take things slow to avoid any mishaps. After coffee and a quick meeting with Mateo, I was ready to meet my Bolivian team.

Felix was the La Paz lead and was responsible for marketing our products in Bolivia. He was already waiting for me in front of my hotel, with the engine idling. It was hard to believe that I was banging on the hotel's front door only a few hours ago. I took an immediate shine to Felix. He was smooth, relaxed, funny, perfect English, and quite sure of himself. He handed me a bag, "A Bolivian breakfast for you; sorry, but we ran out of Dunkin Donuts!" I cautiously peered into the bag; there was a wonderful smell. "OK, Felix, what am I going to eat?" Felix chuckled, "It's called a *Salteñas,* a Bolivian breakfast pastry filled with carrots, potatoes, peas, and meat. It's topped with a sweet sauce and baked. It's delicious; it's a favorite with my children." I hadn't planned on eating lunch this early; I was thinking more about something more traditional, like an egg McMuffin. Felix was right; it was a delicious meal and thank goodness he had plenty of napkins on hand, as I am known to miss the target on more than one occasion.

It was a good morning with a few meetings lined up, and it was a pleasure meeting the local team. I was all prepared to give a short presentation, but just before that, I had to go downstairs for a moment, then quickly ran back up the stairs to the meeting room only to find myself quite literally speechless, out of breath, a victim of altitude sickness. Felix quickly caught on to my lame attempt at hand signaling and swiftly moved on to the next item on the agenda while I eventually caught my breath and could speak.

A much-needed Bolivian lunch

For lunch, Felix and I drove to meet his lovely wife, Maria, who would join us. As we parked and headed to the Mi Teleférico, also known as Teleférico La Paz–El Alto, an aerial cable car urban transit system, I was in for a treat. The goal is to construct an aerial urban transportation system that covers twenty-one miles with eleven lines and thirty stations. I was pretty impressed with the system's efficiency, which is unique in many ways. The trip gave me a unique opportunity to experience the city's dramatic setting. Here is a city spread out over 1,250 square miles; the view was amazing and left me breathless in more ways than one.

I recounted my last cable car adventure to Felix at the Great Wall of China. My back was acting up, which happens occasionally, and my guide quickly suggested we take the little cable car to the next meeting place. I agreed. My guide warned me to step in the middle, not on either side—nothing like a tipsy cable car. To my left was a vast expanse of rolling hills and farms; to my right, the Great Wall was within touching distance. The cable car swayed back and forth like some child toy and groaned as it moved along the wall, higher and higher to reach the tower station. Careful stepping out, please!

View of La Paz by *Teleferico*

After scrutinizing the menu, I went local and chose the *picante de pollo* (spicy chicken), which Felix told me was a popular Bolivian dish originally from Cochabamba. There are probably as many recipes for this spicy chicken dish as Bolivian cooks. Still, the key ingredients in an authentic picante de pollo, aside from the chicken, are Aji Amarillo, the well-known Peruvian chili peppers. I learned firsthand that they pack quite a punch, so buyer beware. With the chicken came *chuño*, a potato native to Bolivia's Andean region. It was all very delicious.

Felix noted that La Paz was founded in 1548 as Nuestra Señora de La Paz ("Our Lady of Peace") by the conquistador Captain

Alonso de Mendoza on the site of an Inca village. The city was renamed La Paz de Ayacucho in 1825, commemorating the last decisive battle in the wars of independence. I always learn from my customers, and this time was no exception. Felix ordered a bottle of Kohlberg Stelar *'Ugni" Blanc*, an excellent choice; a wine with an exotic nose of ripe citrus with just a hint of oak and medium-bodied with some roasted and vanilla notes. According to Felix, Bolivia's wine comes from the Tarija region in the south-center of the country. The wine industry has existed for a few years, let's say, dating back to the 16th century when Spanish colonizers planted vineyards to supply wine for the Catholic church and the mining industry. Strange bedfellows, but wine is wine.

Felix ordered a Quinoa Pudding for dessert, adding that I must have some as it is considered an iconic Bolivian specialty, popular through the Andean highlands. I was going to beg off after hearing "Quinoa," but there was no polite way out or easy back door within reach. The dish has only four ingredients – quinoa, eggs, sugar and raisins. These are baked until they soften and reach a cake-like yet pudding-ey consistency. This is a local delight, Felix reminded. I have encountered plenty of local delight that made me sick just by looking at it. Local cooks are known to give their unique twist to this distinct dessert, such as soaking the quinoa in hot water with cinnamon and sugar to sweeten it. It's that knot in my stomach, thank you.

Tomorrow, I have another full-day meeting with Felix and his team to develop product marketing strategies and how we can make inroads in a challenging market. I have to support their efforts in any way I can. He has a great team of enthusiastic young people dedicated to making the business successful. My meeting with, what I hope will be, my new Chilean team leader went very well. He is aggressive and has an excellent business pedigree. Ultimately, it's all about people and letting them know I care and will support them in any way possible.

I am sure I will be back. After all, my Bolivian visa is good for an entire year!

THE LAST APPOINTMENT

*U*mberto glanced at the man, who gave a nonchalant shrug and said, "It's a sure thing." But Umberto knew better. In this line of work, there was no such thing as certainty. The "Appointment," as they called it, was done clean and efficient, just like the others. And yet, despite wanting to believe the man's casual confidence, Umberto's instincts never let him forget the ever-present uncertainty of their world.

Somewhere along the Bolivian-Argentinian border, the air was still, heavy with the quiet tension of dawn. Umberto had been awake for hours, meticulously running through his mental checklist—a ritual honed over years of doing this job. The man had joked about his "hit list," but for Umberto, it was no laughing matter. Wind speed, direction, light source, range, and temperature—no detail was too small to recheck. Precision was everything. He preferred working alone. In his experience, only one man ever returned when working in pairs.

As the first light touched the horizon, Umberto knew his target would soon emerge. The sound of distant church bells echoed through the valley, marking the hour. He kissed his Virgin Mary medallion, whispering a prayer—not for forgiveness, but for courage, for steadiness. His hands were calm as they cradled the cold steel of his Polish bolt-action sniper rifle, chambered with 7.62x51mm rounds. He adjusted the Leupold 4.5-14x50 scope and settled into position, eyes scanning the village below.

Noon arrived. The sun bathed the square in light as children, dressed in their Sunday best, darted about, laughing. A tall, blond European man, sunglasses hiding his eyes, descended the steps of Las Iglesias de La Santa Maria and joined the crowd. Umberto's breath slowed, his heart a steady drumbeat in his chest. The moment came. He squeezed the trigger with practiced ease.

The target jerked, staggered, then crumpled to the ground in front of the church. The peaceful scene shattered into chaos. Screams filled the air as people scattered in every direction, some pointing wildly, others kneeling in shock. A woman in a yellow dress fell to her knees beside the lifeless body, her fists pounding against it as blood spattered her clothes. Her eyes lifted toward the hills as if she could sense him watching.

But Umberto was already moving. He dismantled the rifle with methodical precision, leaving no trace behind. His escape route was memorized, every step calculated. Another job done. Another clean exit.

He'd completed more assignments than he could remember, and the emotions that had once haunted him—remorse, guilt—were long buried. Early on, those feelings had nearly driven him mad, filling his nights with the faces of his victims. But he had learned to detach and view each mission as a puzzle to solve. It was safer that way, cleaner. Umberto didn't consider himself a bad man. He was a professional, a God-fearing man who was good at what he did. People told him he was "gifted." Yet, beneath the surface, a weariness had begun to creep in, and with it, the quiet fear that he might one day slip.

His contact, Gregory, was never far from his mind. With his shark-like, pale blue eyes and thick Eastern European accent, Gregory was a man Umberto could never trust. Dressed impeccably despite the heat, Gregory always delivered the disassembled rifle with eerie precision, briefing him on the target with cold efficiency. It was all business. And soon, Gregory had hinted, there might be new toys—perhaps a Russian-made rifle or even the Barrett 82A1/M107, the ultimate sniper's weapon.

Umberto smiled at the thought, but the smile didn't reach his eyes. He knew it wouldn't be long before Gregory's next visit. And despite the growing exhaustion in his soul, the work would continue—until, one day, it didn't.

The rendezvous was set in San Sebastián, in the heart of the *Parte Vieja* (Old Town) at Txuleta, a restaurant nestled in the *Plaza de la Trinidad*. The early evening air was warm, but a gentle offshore breeze made it pleasant. As Umberto crossed the square, he thought he glimpsed Gregory seated at a table, though the distance made it hard to be sure. Suddenly, a flock of pigeons scattered skyward, their wings flapping loudly. A sharp glint of light flashed in the corner of his eye, and in the next instant, Umberto jerked, twisted, and collapsed onto the cobbled stones. The sounds around him grew muffled—voices, hurried footsteps, a scream or two—then, only darkness. Amid the confusion, a man wearing a straw hat calmly finished his drink, the lemon slice bobbing in the glass, before rising from his seat and casually leaving behind a neatly wrapped, empty box on the chair.

Part III

RECIPES

THOUGHTS ON THE RECIPES FROM THE AMERICAS

*O*nce again, this collection of recipes offers an irresistibly diverse, vibrant, and enticing array of dishes. My previous books leaned on French cuisine and its derivatives, this time, I've broadened my horizons by incorporating a touch of Southern cooking. My passion for authentic Southern food is deeply ingrained with family roots tracing back to the 1600s in Maryland and the Carolinas. Naturally, Maryland's Eastern Shore and New Orleans had to be featured—their unique fusion of cultures makes them a culinary haven imbued with subtle French influences. Dishes like the rich and comforting New Orleans Shrimp and Grits and the indulgent Bananas Foster for dessert are among the highlights. And, of course, let's not forget the Champagne!

I've gathered some remarkable dishes from my travels throughout Latin America this time. The tender Grilled Octopus from Cancun, Mexico, was simply unforgettable, while the bold, fiery flavors of the Peruvian Spicy Chicken from Lima brought a thrilling depth to this collection. And naturally, the classic Peruvian Pisco Sour cocktail makes an appearance—too delicious to leave out! Too tasty to have just one! For a grand finale, I've included Brazilian-style Osso Buco, inspired by the kitchens of

São Paulo, a melt-in-your-mouth masterpiece that's nothing short of extraordinary.

Exploring diverse cuisines, wines, and cultures is an inseparable journey. I invite you to savor the food and wine selections I've curated and join me in celebrating the endless joys of culinary discovery.

AMERICAN CUISINE
CREAMED ONIONS GRATIN

Imagine being transported to England in the 1920s, where a typical meal might feature creamed onions alongside a hearty slab of beef. Although the English claim this comforting dish, France and Italy assert their culinary influence over its origin. These small, flavorful onions were so treasured across Europe that they eventually made their way to American tables, becoming a cherished part of our culinary traditions.

You might wonder why we're discussing creamed onions when Thanksgiving is still a distant thought. But certain foods—especially comfort foods—are deeply tied to family traditions, weaving into the fabric of our celebrations. It's almost instinctual. Imagine the disappointment if Grandma Mildred showed up without her famous green Jell-O salad or Aunt Minnie forgot her gingerbread turkey-shaped cookies, which always disappear long before dessert. It just wouldn't feel right, would it?

How could anyone attend a family dinner without bringing their signature dish—whether it's adored or secretly dreaded? Traditions like these can become so ingrained that breaking them feels almost unthinkable. What, no French wine this time? But you always bring French wine! Australian or Chilean wine? What's happening to tradition?

You probably understand this better than most if you've hosted a holiday meal or prepared a feast. Traditions are important—no doubt about that. But we don't have to be bound by them, repeating the same dishes or routines out of habit, like Pavlovian dogs. Why not enjoy creamed onions or roast turkey on a random Tuesday, perhaps paired with champagne? We don't need a special occasion to enjoy a glass of bubbly, and we certainly don't have to wait for Aunt Gertrude's passing or Little Tim's graduation to pop open the good stuff (French, of course).

So here's my call to action: let's shake up our culinary routines and break through those self-imposed barriers! Serve creamed onions on any night of the week. Pair turkey with champagne, even when it's not Thanksgiving. Life is worth celebrating—why not do it with every meal?

Creamed Onion Gratin
SERVES 6–8
(thanks in part to Saveur Magazine)

Ingredients
Two medium yellow onions, cored and quartered lengthwise
¼ cup olive oil
Kosher salt and freshly ground black pepper, to taste
2 tbsp. unsalted butter
2 tbsp. flour
1 cup heavy cream
¼ cup dry white wine
Freshly grated nutmeg, to taste
½ cup finely grated Parmesan
3 oz. Gorgonzola, crumbled
¼ tsp. paprika

Instructions
Heat oven to 350°. Toss onions with oil in a 9″ × 11″ baking dish and season with salt and pepper. Bake, stirring occasionally, until soft and lightly browned, about 1 hour; set aside. Heat oven to broil.

Heat butter in a 2-qt. saucepan over medium-high heat; add flour, and cook, stirring, until smooth, about 1 minute. Add cream and wine, and cook, stirring, until thickened, about 5 minutes—season sauce with salt, pepper, and nutmeg.

Pour the sauce evenly over the onions. Sprinkle with Parmesan, dot with Gorgonzola, and sprinkle with paprika; broil until the cheese is melted and golden brown on top, about 2 minutes.

Close the house curtains and fill a large bowl with creamed onions. Settle back, spoon in hand. No one needs to know.

Now, about those wines…

Guilhem and Goisot Bourgogne Aligote, Burgundy, France

Domaine Pierre Frick Chasselas Vinifie, Alsace, France

Chateau Haut Brion Graves Pessac Leognan Wine, Bordeaux, France

St. Innocent Winery Pinot Blanc, Freedom Hill Vineyard Willamette Valley, Oregon

Veuve Clicquot Yellow Label. Perhaps a bit pricey, but oh, what pleasure!!

Pan-Seared Snow Goose Breasts, Peppers and Onions

As served tableside at Spaniard Neck Farm

Ingredients:

Four servings

Four boneless snow goose breast halves, skin removed

¼ cup olive oil

Two teaspoons of Worcestershire sauce

½ teaspoon garlic salt

One teaspoon hot pepper sauce (Tabasco)

One medium yellow onion, thinly sliced

One green bell pepper, coarsely chopped

One red bell pepper, coarsely chopped

two jalapeno peppers, seeded and minced
Two garlic cloves, thinly sliced
One cup of tomatoes, seeded and chopped
Salt and pepper to taste

Directions:

I have a rule of thumb when cooking wild game birds. If the bird takes flight, it's not fully cooked or ready to serve your guests. Before serving, check for visual signs of doneness; juices should run clear, and meat should be fork-tender. A thermometer is the only reliable way to ensure safety and determine the "doneness" of meat and poultry. To be safe, it must be cooked to an internal temperature high enough to destroy any harmful bacteria that may have been in the food. With that disclaimer out of the way, you can eat it raw for all I care.

Carefully slice the goose breasts thinly across the "grain" of the meat. Combine half of the olive oil, Worcestershire sauce, garlic salt, and hot pepper sauce in a glass bowl. Add sliced goose, cover, and refrigerate for 1 to 2 hours. This little interruption allows you to check on the quality of the wines. How else can you explain to your guest the subtleties of each wine? Heat the remaining oil in a large skillet over medium heat when cooking. Add onion, peppers, and garlic. Cook until onions are medium brown. Remove the goose from the marinade. Drain well and discard the marinade. Add goose and stir-fry for 1 to 2 minutes or until just cooked or no further honking is heard, but not past medium-rare. Stir in tomato and season to taste with salt, pepper, and additional hot sauce. Serve over a bed of Cajun rice. A nice little green Boston lettuce salad in oil and vinegar would be just the right touch. A fresh, crusty baguette would be nice, along with a selection of cheeses, perhaps a *Camembert de Normandie*, a *Bleu d'Auvergne* , and a *Chevrotin de Savoie.*

Now, about those wines...

DeLoach Russian River Valley Ritchie Vineyard Chardonnay 2007

Churton Pinot Noir Marlborough 2009, New Zealand

David Bruce Pinot Noir Sonoma Coast 2011

Leyda Reserva Syrah 2011 Leyda Valley, Chile

Château Thivin Les Sept Vignes 2011 Côte de Brouilly, Beaujolais, France

Beef Diane in a Rich Cognac Sauce

Ingredients:

Four beef tenderloin steaks (about six ounces each). Don't skip on quality here.

Salt and freshly ground black pepper to taste

Two tablespoons unsalted butter (more butter is allowed)
One shallot, finely chopped
One clove of garlic, minced
¼ cup cognac or brandy (I choose cognac as only a purist would)
One cup of beef broth
Two teaspoons of Dijon mustard
¼ cup heavy cream (a truly magic ingredient)
One teaspoon of Worcestershire sauce
Two tablespoons chopped fresh parsley.
One tablespoon of chopped fresh chives.

Directions:

Season the steaks with salt and pepper.

In a large skillet, melt butter over medium-high heat. Add the steaks and sear until golden brown, about 3–4 minutes per side for medium-rare. Remove the steaks from the skillet and set aside.

Add the shallot, garlic, and sauté until softened in the same skillet for about 2 minutes. If you have a daring bone in your body, may I suggest adding some mushrooms and cooking for 3–5 minutes? This will add some additional flavor.

Carefully pour the cognac to deglaze the pan, scraping up any browned bits from the bottom. Allow the cognac to reduce by half.

Stir in the beef broth, Dijon mustard, and Worcestershire sauce. Bring to a simmer and cook until the sauce is slightly reduced, about 3 minutes.

Stir in the heavy cream and return the steaks to the skillet. Cook for another 2–3 minutes until the steaks are heated through and the sauce has thickened.

Garnish with chopped parsley and chives before serving.

Prep Time: 10 minutes | Cooking Time: 20 minutes | Total Time: 30 minutes

Now, about those wines...

Let's be honest and recognize that Steak Diane is about richness and savory flavors, so don't think about light wines. You need a wine with depth and structure. Think about these when you shop for wines:

Pomerol for its smooth texture and concentrated fruit

Cabernet Sauvignon from Sonoma for its vibrant and spicy notes

Baga, from Portugal, is for those not afraid to explore wines that may be off the beaten path and far from your 7–11. Like Pinot Noir, Baga provides a bold and tart option that pairs wonderfully with the steak's robust profile. I might add that it is at an attractive price point.

New Orleans Shrimp and Grits

Now, being served in Heaven!

Ingredients

One ½ pounds jumbo shrimp, peeled and deveined

Three tablespoons of Dijon mustard

One pinch of seafood seasoning (such as Old Bay®), or to taste

Two ½ cups heavy whipping cream

Two ½ cups chicken stock

One shallot, finely chopped
Three tablespoons butter
One teaspoon of garlic powder
One cup of regular grits, uncooked
salt and ground black pepper to taste
Twelve slices of maple-cured bacon
One loa¼ cup olive oil, divided
One l¾ cup shredded Cheddar cheese
One loaf of Italian bread
¼ cup olive oil, divided
¾ cup shredded Cheddar cheese

Directions

Preheat oven to 200 degrees F (95 degrees C).

Toss shrimp in a bowl with Dijon mustard until coated, then sprinkle with seafood seasoning. Refrigerate the shrimp while you complete the remaining steps.

Pour cream and chicken stock into a large pot and bring to a boil. Reduce heat to medium-low; stir in shallot, butter, garlic powder, and grits. Bring the mixture to a simmer and cook until the grits have absorbed the liquid and are thick and smooth, for about 20 minutes. Season with salt and black pepper.

"Grits are simply ground corn," says Chef Maulsby. It's genuinely as simplistic as that! They're made from ground white corn called hominy, which means that the hull of the corn was removed by soaking in an alkaline (something that has a basic pH and is therefore not acidic) substance. With southern roots, grits are usually something that I always welcome at restaurants—a staple of southern living.

Place bacon in a large, deep skillet and cook over medium-high heat, turning occasionally, until evenly browned, about 10 minutes. Drain the bacon slices on a paper towel-lined plate.

Wrap Italian bread in aluminum foil and place it in a preheated oven to heat for about 10 minutes. When the bread is hot, and the outside is slightly crunchy, slice it into triangles. Cut the triangles horizontally, place them on a baking sheet, and brush them with two tablespoons of olive oil. Return to the oven to toast for about 5 minutes; remove and keep warm.

Pour two more tablespoons of olive oil into the skillet with bacon drippings and place the skillet over medium-high heat. Cook and stir shrimp until pink and no longer translucent inside, about 5 minutes.

Divide the grits among six serving bowls and arrange the cooked shrimp around the edges of the bowls. Place each bowl on a serving plate with two slices of bacon and two toast triangles. Sprinkle the grits with shredded Cheddar cheese.

Now, about those wines…

Veuve Clicquot Champagne (moderately priced, so you don't have to order a bottle of Louis Roederer, which can run you a little over $400.00) Unless you want to!

Sonoma Coast Chardonnay, more than just a California memory.

Chablis (crisp acidity) is a real surprise if you like wines from *Bourgogne.*

And consider a Gewürztraminer (you are no longer invading Alsace, again, an excellent pairing suggestion.)

BANANAS FOSTER
(A New Orleans Tradition)

This is a dessert to die for, literally—that is if you are not careful lighting the alcohol. Trust me on this: one eyebrow missing is no laughing matter! Bananas Foster is a dessert made from bananas and vanilla ice cream, with a sauce made from butter, brown sugar, cinnamon, dark rum, and banana liqueur. The butter, sugar, and bananas are cooked, and alcohol is added and ignited. The bananas and sauce are then served over the ice cream.

(Serves 4)

Ingredients
¼ cup (½ stick) butter
One cup of brown sugar
½ teaspoon cinnamon
¼ cup banana liqueur
¼ cup dark Cuban rum
Four scoops of vanilla ice cream
Four bananas, cut in half, lengthwise, then halved

Directions
Combine the butter, sugar, and cinnamon in a flambé pan or skillet. Place the pan on top of the stove over low heat and cook, stirring, until the sugar dissolves.

Stir in the banana liqueur, then place the bananas in the pan.

When the banana sections soften and brown, carefully add the rum.

Then, tip the pan slightly and ignite the rum. *Viva la revolución.* (When the flames subside, lift the bananas out of the pan and place four pieces over each portion of ice cream. Generously spoon warm sauce over the top of the ice cream and serve immediately.

Prepare for a second round of servings! Bring the bottle of Rum to the table!

GRILLADES 'N' GRITS

This delicious recipe is thanks to Alpana Beiser and liberally taken from *Gypsyplate*. This is one smart cookie, to be sure—grillades over creamy grits. I had to sit down for a moment. My heart was racing but in a good way! This dish goes hand-in-hand with the two delights from New Orleans. Man, do they know how to enjoy the sweet life? Grillades, from the French, *bien sur*, are medallions of meat pan-fried and then gently braised in a rich tomato-based gravy. Help me, Rhonda!

Grillades

1.5 lbs top round, cut into 2" cubes, then beaten to one-half in thick
½ cup flour
1 tsp salt
2 tsp Creole seasoning
¼ cup oil

Gravy

1 Tbsp oil
One celery stalk, chopped
One onion, chopped
One-half green bell pepper, chopped
One-half red bell pepper, chopped
Four cloves garlic, finely chopped
2 Tbsp butter
3 Tbsp flour
1.5 cups beef broth
One can of diced tomatoes
½ cup red wine
2 tsp Creole seasoning
1 tsp red chili flakes
1 tsp dried thyme
1 tsp dried oregano
Four bay leaves
1 tsp hot sauce

Grits

One cup grits
Two cups water
Two cups milk
1 tsp salt
1.5 cup shredded cheddar cheese

Instructions

Grillades

Cut meat into 2" cubes. Pound with a mallet until they are about one-half" thick.

Combine ½ cup flour, 2 tsp Creole seasoning, and 1 tsp salt and spread on a plate. Dredge meat medallions in the flour mixture.

Heat ¼ cup oil in a large skillet, preferably cast iron, over medium-high heat.

Place medallions in hot oil and fry until browned on each side. If necessary, cook in batches rather than overcrowding.

Remove to a plate and set aside.

Gravy

In the same pan, add the remaining 1 Tbsp oil. Add chopped onions, celery, and bell pepper and saute until the onions are translucent, about 5 minutes.

Add garlic, stir, and cook for an additional minute.

Reduce the heat to medium and push the vegetables to one side of the pan. Add butter; once it is melted, stir in flour to form a roux. Mix the vegetables into the roux mixture.

Slowly add beef broth, stirring continuously to avoid clumping.

Add wine, tomatoes, Creole seasoning, red chili flakes, salt, thyme, oregano, hot sauce, and bay leaves. And mix everything well.

Place grillades in gravy and bring to a simmer. Cover, reduce heat to low, and simmer for 1.5 hours.

Grits

In a medium saucepan, bring water, milk, and salt to a low boil over medium-high heat. Stir frequently to prevent the milk from scorching on the pan's bottom.

Slowly stir in grits to avoid clumping.

Reduce heat to low, cover, and cook for the time indicated on the package, stirring occasionally, until the grits are cooked. If they get too thick, add more water.

Once cooked, stir in shredded cheese.

Now, about those wines…

Willamette Valley Chardonnay – The key word here is "Willamette."

Picpoul de Pinet from the South of France (one of my favorites and so drinkable)

Cabernet Sauvignon, no room for misunderstanding.

Cote-du-Rhone Village (excellent); choosing this shows you are not fooling around.

Pork Tenderloin with Merlot, Shallots and Blackberry Sauce

*T*his all-American recipe is fabulously simple to assemble and guaranteed to have your guests begging for your culinary secrets. I have done this countless times, and it never gets old, unlike me. It's the kind of dish you can whip up effortlessly—perhaps even with a martini in one hand and a spatula in the other. I was kidding, of course. I prefer cooking with a glass of French wine on one hand and a healthy dose of attitude on the other. Naturally.

Tenderloin is one of my favorites, but this recipe deserves a special salute. It never fails to deliver consistent, mouthwatering results. Try it out, and let me know what you think.

Back in the day, Monsieur Louis, my trusty golden partner, would glide across the kitchen floor with the precision of a German U-boat commander patrolling the Atlantic, and this dish was one of his favorites. That should speak volumes.

SERVES 4

Ingredients

This recipe is as elegant as it is quick and easy to prepare for an evening meal.

Two pork tenderloins (about 1 lb each)

One tablespoon of olive oil, divided

One tablespoon chopped fresh rosemary leaf

½ teaspoon salt, divided

½ teaspoon freshly ground pepper, divided

Four shallots, minced

One clove of garlic, minced

1 cup merlot or dry red wine

One tablespoon of chicken stock powder or chicken soup base (a concentrated, reduced chicken broth can be substituted)

Two tablespoons of cherry preserves or blackberry preserves

Two tablespoons butter

Directions

Preheat oven to 350.

Coat pork with 1 ½ tsp olive oil; rub with rosemary, ¼ tsp salt and ¼ tsp pepper.

Heat a heavy, ovenproof skillet over high heat.

Cook pork, turning often, until lightly browned on all sides, 5 minutes.

Transfer skillet and pork to oven; roast until thermometer reads 150 degrees, about 25–35 minutes. This will vary with each oven, so I use the cooking thermometer as my guide, especially with pork (*because you can never be too careful with pork – thanks, Mom*)

Transfer cooked pork to a platter; keep warm.

Add remaining 1 ½ tsp oil to the same skillet.

Heat over medium heat.

Add shallots and garlic; cook, stirring, until lightly browned, about 4 minutes.

Add wine; cook over high heat until reduced by half, about 5 minutes.

Reduce heat to medium.

Stir in stock concentrate and preserves.

Add remaining ¼ tsp each salt and pepper; adjust seasoning if necessary.

Whisk in butter.

Pour into a serving bowl.

Slice pork into ¼" slices and serve with sauce.

Serve with baby red potatoes and a green salad with vinaigrette dressing. Yum!!

Note: Rather than pouring the sauce, I have started cutting the tenderloin into medallions while in the pan. That way, every medallion is thoroughly coated with the delicious sauce. I think it's a better way of doing it and guaranteed to please your guests. On the other hand, the amount of pork will have diminished when it reaches the table—one of the great mysteries of our time!

Now, about that wine

Pinot Noir has long been known to dance well with this dish.

Pinot Blanc, if you would prefer to keep a good Red away, that is no one's business but yours.

Côte de Beaune (Burgundy) It is a tasty region of France. Saint-Amour (Beaujolais), I have no question about which bottle I am reaching for.

Bison Strip Steak with a Spicy Red Onion Marmalade

From Blue Canyon Kitchen and Tavern, Cleveland, OH
—*Chef Brandt Evans*

*Y*es, saddle up, ladies and gentlemen. This is a hearty dish, perhaps not one for the dainty palate, meek and mild, or politically upsetting kind. While you can pair a good wine with this dish, I favor a six-pack of cold beer for starters. Join me!

Ingredients

8–10 oz Bison Strip Steak
Four medium Red Onion
One ½ c Sugar
2 T Red Curry Paste
One can of Unsweetened Coconut milk
1T minced Garlic
1T chopped fresh Rosemary

Directions

Season Bison Strip Steak generously with salt and black pepper on both sides.

Place on a heated grill; cook each side for about 5 minutes to achieve a Medium Rare to Medium or about 130 internal temperature.

In a sauce pot, add olive oil and sauté onions and garlic till translucent.

Add sugar, coconut milk, and curry paste (if you do not like spicy food, do not add Curry Paste or cut it in half) and whisk until the paste is dissolved.

Reduce until you have a thick glaze consistency, and fold in fresh chopped Rosemary.

Place Steak on a plate, top with the Red Onion Marmalade, and serve.

Pop a cold beer!

Now, about those wines…these are commonly found on the wild prairie

Pinot Noir (Willamette Valley) Unmatched

Malbec (Mendoza, Argentina) A beautiful wine, a beautiful region.

Tempranillo (Rioja, Spain) is a beautiful wine. I suggest you try it with El Cid before your next encounter with the Saracens.

Syrah (Rhône Valley, France)

Tuscan Sangiovese (Chianti Classico Italy) Think "blood of Jupiter".

LATIN AMERICAN CUISINE

GRILLED OCTOPUS –
CANCUN, MEXICO

Pulpo a la parrilla de Yucatán

Ingredients:
Three pounds of cleaned octopus
One bay leaf
Four thyme branches

twenty peppercorns
Salt and freshly ground black pepper to taste
One head of garlic, cut in half
Three lemons
Three tablespoons extra-virgin olive oil
Minced parsley for garnish

Instructions

Combine the octopus, bay leaf, thyme, peppercorns, one teaspoon salt, garlic, and one of the lemons, cut in half, in a saucepan, and water to cover. Turn the heat to medium, cover, and bring to a boil. Adjust the heat so that the liquid simmers, and cook until the octopus is tender, 30 to 90 minutes (check with the point of a sharp knife). Drain, discarding all the solids (except for the octopus). You can prepare this 24 hours before this point; cover and refrigerate the octopus.

Start a charcoal or wood fire or preheat a gas grill; the fire should be quite hot, and the grill rack should be about four inches from the heat source. Cut the octopus into large serving pieces, brush it with half the olive oil, and sprinkle it with salt and pepper. Grill it quickly so that the outside browns before the inside dries out. Cut the remaining lemon into wedges.

Brush the octopus with the remaining olive oil. Serve with lemon wedges, hot or at room temperature, garnished with parsley.

Now, about those wines…

Kir-Yianni Assyrtiko is a crisp and minerally white wine from Greece. It's almost the perfect wine to pair with this dish. It has flavors of lemon, green apple, and a distinct volcanic minerality. Track it down!

Burgans is an Albarino from Spain's Rias Baixas region, known for its crisp and aromatic wines. This white wine offers flavors of green apple, citrus, and a hint of salinity, making it an excellent companion for seafood, especially shellfish. It is a sure bet and will not offend anyone.

Louis Jadot Petit Chablis is a French white wine known for its crisp and mineral-driven character. It presents flavors of citrus green apple and a distinct chalky quality. I personally love a French Chablis. Yes, I will proudly show my true colors.

CHILAQUILES – MEXICO CITY

Yield: four servings

Ingredients
For The Roasted Salsa Verde
Four medium tomatillos, husks removed
½ small onion
Two garlic cloves peeled
1 to 2 small serrano chiles, stems removed
One cilantro sprig

Salt
For The Tortilla Chips (Optional; See Tip)
Five tablespoons of neutral oil (such as sunflower or grapeseed)
Eight corn tortillas, each sliced into six wedges
Salt
¼ teaspoon chili powder
For The Chilaquiles
Three tablespoons neutral oil (such as sunflower or grapeseed)
One small onion, sliced into rings
¾ cup/3 ounces crumbled queso fresco
Salt and black pepper
Eight large eggs
½ cup Mexican *crema* or sour cream
½ cup cilantro leaves

Preparation

Prepare the *salsa verde* (optional): Arrange a rack six inches from the broiler and set the broiler to high. Set a half-sheet pan lined with foil on the rack. Heat for 5 minutes.

Prepare the *salsa verde* (optional): Arrange a rack six inches from the broiler and set the broiler to high. Set a half-sheet pan lined with foil on the rack. Heat for 5 minutes.

Carefully add tomatillos, onion, garlic, and chiles to the pan. Broil until blistered and charred, 10 to 14 minutes, turning once halfway through.

Prepare the tortilla chips (optional): Heat a medium cast-iron or nonstick skillet over medium and add five tablespoons oil. Cook tortillas in batches, frying until golden and crisp, 3 to 4 minutes per batch.

Transfer tortillas to a wire rack or paper towels to drain, then place in a medium bowl. Season with salt and chili powder and toss. Taste and season accordingly. Once the oil has cooled, wipe out and reserve the skillet.

Prepare the chilaquiles: Heat 2 tablespoons oil over medium in a large skillet, then add the *salsa verde*. (It should simmer upon contacting the pan.) Simmer for 2 minutes, then taste and season with salt.

Stir in the onion, then add half of the tortilla chips and half of the queso fresco and toss to combine. Taste and season with salt, add the remaining tortilla chips and toss again. Lower heat and cook until heated through.

Heat the remaining tablespoon of oil over medium in the reserved medium skillet. I work in batches, frying the eggs and cooking to my preferred doneness.

Divide the chilaquiles among plates. Top each with the remaining queso fresco, two fried eggs, two dollops of crema, and cilantro leaves. Customize as you please!

VERACRUZAN SEAFOOD COCKTAIL

(*Vuelve a La Vida*)

Ingredients

Three bay leaves

One head of garlic, halved crosswise

One lb. large shrimp, peeled and deveined

One lb. cleaned calamari, bodies cut into one-sixth"-wide rings, tentacles halved lengthwise

12 oz. boneless, skinless red snapper filets

¾ cup fresh lime juice

2 tsp. dried oregano, preferably Mexican

Kosher salt, to taste

One lb. plum tomatoes, cored, seeded, and finely chopped

One cup ketchup

One cup of tomato juice

One cup pimiento-stuffed green olives

One cup finely chopped cilantro

¼ cup Worcestershire

6 tbsp. olive oil

Two serrano chiles, stemmed and thinly sliced

One habanero or Scotch bonnet chile, stemmed, seeded, and minced

One medium white onion, finely chopped

Sixteen small oysters, shucked, juices reserved

Sixteen small clams, shucked, juices reserved

Two avocados, thinly sliced

Saltine crackers for serving

Instructions

In a 4-qt saucepan, bring bay leaves, garlic, and eight cups of water to a boil. Add shrimp and cook until pink, about 2 minutes. Transfer to a cutting board and cut into one" pieces; set aside in a bowl.

Add calamari bodies and tentacles to boiling water; cook until just cooked through, about 1 minute. Drain and transfer to bowl with shrimp; set aside. In another bowl, combine snapper, half the lime juice, and oregano; season with salt and let sit until fish is opaque, about 20 minutes. Drain and set aside.

In a bowl, whisk together the remaining lime juice with tomatoes, ketchup, tomato juice, olives, cilantro, Worcestershire, oil, serrano and habanero chiles, and onion; add reserved shrimp and calamari, snapper, oysters, and clams with their juices and fold gently to combine—season with salt. Serve seafood cocktails in large goblets or bowls, with slices of avocado and Saltine crackers on the side.

Now, about those wines…

This mystery is straightforward to solve with only one word: Champagne!

Veuve Clicquot Yellow Label Brut, (France) The widow never knew how famous she was.

La Marca Prosecco (Italy) A Prosecco is a fine sparkling wine always good to have in your refrigerator in the event of an unexpected guest.

J Vineyards California Cuvee Sparkling Wines (California)

Cupcake Vineyards Prosecco, (Italy)

PANAMANIAN *SANCOCHO*

In presenting this dish, I salute two of my dear former customers, one in Panama and the other in Bogota, Colombia. I hold the memories of our time spent together in my heart.

Panamanian Sancocho

Sancocho is the national dish of Panama and a very local dish in Colombia. It is delicious and typically made with chicken and vegetables.

Ingredients
Nine cups water
One whole chicken

Two plantains peeled and cut into 2-inch pieces
One onion, chopped
½ cup chopped fresh cilantro
Five cloves garlic, chopped
One ½ teaspoon salt
Three pounds of yuca (cassava) roots, peeled and cut into 1-inch cubes
Six small red potatoes, quartered
1 (15.25 ounce) can of corn, drained

Directions

Prepare the base: In a large pot, combine 8 cups of water, chicken (preferably bone-in pieces), two ripe plantains (peeled and cut into chunks), one large onion (quartered), a handful of fresh cilantro, four garlic cloves (minced), and 1 tablespoon of salt. Bring to a boil over high heat.

Simmer the chicken: Once boiling, reduce the heat to medium-low and simmer uncovered for about 45 minutes or until the chicken is cooked. To check, insert an instant-read thermometer into the thickest part of the thigh (near the bone); it should read 165°F (74°C).

Remove and cool the chicken: Using tongs, carefully remove the chicken from the pot and let it cool slightly on a plate.

Add the root vegetables: To the same pot, add 2 cups of yuca (peeled and cut into chunks), two large potatoes (peeled and cubed), and two ears of corn (cut into 3-inch pieces). Cook over medium heat for about 30 minutes or until the yuca and potatoes are tender.

Shred the chicken: Discard the chicken's skin and bones while the vegetables cook , and shred the meat into bite-sized pieces.

To finish the soup, Return the shredded chicken to the pot. Stir well to combine all the ingredients, and simmer for another 5 minutes to allow the flavors to meld.

Taste and adjust: Taste the soup, adding more salt if necessary to adjust the seasoning. For extra flavor, garnish with fresh cilantro or a squeeze of lime before serving.

Now, about those wines…

These three solid wines pair exceptionally well with this dish.

Cava, Spain

Sonoma Chardonnay, California

Rosé from Bandol, South of France

Peruvian Spicy Chicken, Lima Style

Peruvian Roasted Chicken With Spicy Cilantro Sauce

Ingredients

Yield: four servings

FOR THE CHICKEN

Six garlic cloves, finely grated or minced
Three tablespoons soy sauce
One tablespoon of aji Amarillo paste or another chile paste such as sriracha or sambal
One tablespoon of lime juice
One teaspoon *aji panca* paste or one teaspoon *papilla* chili powder
One teaspoon of Dijon mustard
One teaspoon of ground cumin
One teaspoon of freshly ground black pepper
½ teaspoon fine sea salt
1 (3½- to four½-pound) chicken, halved (see Note) or four pounds bone-in, skin-on chicken parts
Extra-virgin olive oil, as needed
Six garlic clov

FOR THE SAUCE

One cup of cilantro leaves and tender stems
3 to 4 jalapeños, seeded and diced
¼ cup/1 ounce crumbled feta cheese
One garlic clove, chopped
One ½tablespoons lime juice, more to taste
Two teaspoons chopped fresh oregano or basil
¾ teaspoon fine sea salt, more to taste
½ teaspoon Dijon mustard
½ tablespoon aji amarillo or other chile paste (see headnote)
½ teaspoon honey
½ teaspoon ground cumin

½ cup extra-virgin olive oil
Lime wedges for garnish

Directions

For the marinade: In a large bowl, whisk together garlic, soy sauce, *aji amarillo* paste, lime juice, *aji panca* paste, mustard, cumin, pepper and salt.

Add chicken halves, turning to coat them all over with marinade. Cover and refrigerate for at least 2 hours and up to 12 hours.

Heat the oven to 450 degrees. Remove chicken from marinade and pat dry with paper towels. Arrange skin-side up on a rimmed baking sheet and drizzle with oil.

Roast until the skin is golden and the chicken is cooked through, 35 to 45 minutes (if using chicken parts, remove the breasts after 25 to 35 minutes). Remove from the oven and let sit, loosely covered with foil, for 10 minutes before serving.

While the chicken is roasting, make the sauce. Blend cilantro, jalapeños, feta, garlic, lime juice, oregano, salt, mustard, aji amarillo paste, honey, and cumin until smooth. With the motor running, slowly drizzle in oil until the mixture is emulsified. Taste and adjust the seasonings with salt, lime juice, or both.

Carve the chicken with seasoned potatoes and serve with the sauce and lime wedges on the side.

Now, About Those Wines...

Arabella Sauvignon Blanc, South Africa
David Marchesi Provare California Sauvignon Blanc
Tom Shula California Chardonnay

TIP

- *To cut a chicken in half, use a sturdy pair of poultry shears to cut lengthwise through the breastbone. Turn over and cut again along the backbone. If desired, cut along the other side of the backbone and remove it.*

Classic Peruvian Pisco Sour Cocktail

There's nothing quite as grand as savoring a perfectly crafted Pisco Sour at your favorite hotel bar in Lima, Peru. You sit, waiting for your client to arrive, each moment filled with anticipation. Of course, a few always turn their noses up at the thought of an egg white in a cocktail—how unfortunate. Little do they know, this drink is dangerously smooth, and pisco has a way of creeping up on you with that unmistakable Peruvian charm. But in the end, you'll be the judge. Stumbling off the bar stool may indicate you've had too much.

Ingredients

Two ounces pisco
1-ounce simple syrup
Three-fourths ounce key lime juice (preferred), or lime juice
One large egg white
2 to 3 dashes of aromatic bitters

Directions

Add the pisco, simple syrup, lime juice, and egg white to a cocktail shaker.

Add ice to fill the shaker and shake vigorously. If you don't have a shaker, you can use a blender. Strain into an old-fashioned or sour glass and sprinkle the bitters on the foam.

Serve immediately and enjoy.

Argentinian-Style Grilled Rib-Eye with Chimichurri Sauce

Yield: four servings

Ingredients
2(1½-inch-thick) bone-in rib-eye steaks, about one¼ pounds each
Two teaspoons of coarse kosher salt
Black pepper, as needed
Extra-virgin olive oil, as needed

Two ounces of creamy blue cheese, such as Jasper Hill Bayley
Hazen Blue
One tablespoon of unsalted butter
Two teaspoons finely chopped chives
Hot sauce, as needed

Directions

Season steaks with salt and pepper for at least 30 minutes and up
to 1 hour before cooking. Cover loosely with plastic wrap and let
stand at room temperature.

Heat grill to high. If using a charcoal grill, mound coals to
one side, allowing for an area of indirect heat. If using a gas grill,
turn on only a few burners and leave the rest off for indirect heat.

Lightly oil the steaks. Place them on the hottest part of the
grill. Cook, covered, until they develop a golden-brown crust,
2 to 3 minutes per side. Move the steaks to indirect heat and
crumble cheese over the top; cover and cook 2 to 5 minutes
longer, depending on the desired doneness. (Pull the meat at 125
degrees for rare.)

Transfer steaks to a cutting board to rest, loosely covered with
foil, for 10 minutes. While the steaks rest, stir together butter,
chives, and hot sauce. Pour over the steak before serving.

Now, about those wines…

A Spanish Malbec brings the rich fruit flavors you're craving, with
a deep, inviting aroma and a silky, smooth finish. Its bold fruity
profile, complemented by aromatic citrus notes, pairs exceptionally well with a perfectly grilled ribeye.

For a more robust option, the California Cabernet Sauvignon is a bold, full-bodied wine that epitomizes the essence of a great Cabernet. With its deep ruby hue and a bouquet of cherries, plums, and violets, this wine delivers a rich and layered experience.

Finally, I recommend a French Merlot because it can cut through the meat's richness while its vibrant fruitiness enhances and elevates the flavors on your plate.

Each of these wines is a sure winner and deserves a gold medal at your table.

CHIMICHURRI SAUCE

Ingredients

3 to 6 coarsely chopped garlic cloves

Two tablespoons coarsely chopped red onion

Two cups coarsely chopped fresh flat-leaf parsley, firmly packed

¼ cup coarsely chopped fresh cilantro, optional

¼ cup coarsely chopped fresh oregano or one teaspoon dried oregano, optional

One tablespoon of freshly squeezed lime juice, or to taste

Two tablespoons red wine vinegar, or to taste
Two and 3/4 cup olive oil
Kosher salt, to taste
Red pepper flakes, to taste

Directions

In a food processor, pulse the garlic and red onion until they are finely chopped.

Add the parsley, cilantro, and oregano, as desired. Pulse briefly until the herbs are finely chopped.

Transfer the mixture to a serving bowl. Stir in the lime juice, red wine vinegar, and olive oil.

Season with salt and red pepper flakes to taste. Cover and store in the refrigerator until ready to serve. Enjoy.

BRAZIL

Moqueca (Brazilian Seafood Stew)

Ingredients

Yield: 4 to 6 servings
Six head-on prawns or large head-on shrimp (about twelve ounces)
12 ounces cod fillet, cut into 1-inch pieces
Kosher salt
Two limes

Three tablespoons *dendê* oil (red palm oil; see Note)

Four garlic cloves, minced

One small yellow onion, chopped (1 cup)

Eight ounces sweet baby bell peppers or two bell peppers, any color, sliced into ¼-inch strips (2 cups)

One pound of fresh tomatoes, cut in 1-inch-wide wedges (2½ cups)

One whole hot chili, such as red Scotch bonnet or bird's eye, pierced all over with the tip of a knife

1(13.5-ounce) can full-fat coconut milk

¼cup chopped fresh cilantro

Steamed rice for serving

Farofa – a traditional Brazilian side dish made with toasted yuca flour/cassava flour.

Directions

Use a pair of kitchen scissors to cut along the length of each prawn deep enough to expose and remove the vein. Place the fish chunks in a large bowl and season with one teaspoon salt. Squeeze in the juice of one lime and toss to coat. Set the prawns and fish aside while preparing the sauce.

In a large, shallow Dutch oven or large, deep skillet, melt three tablespoons *dendê* oil over medium heat. Add the garlic and cook, stirring, until softened and fragrant, 1 minute. Add the onion, stir and cook, stirring until translucent, about 2 minutes.

Increase the heat to high, add the peppers, tomatoes, and chile, and season with salt. Cook, stirring frequently, until the peppers are softened and any liquid from the tomatoes is beginning to evaporate, 4 minutes.

Pour the coconut milk, stir, and reduce the heat to medium. Simmer, stirring occasionally, until the liquid thickens and reduces to a creamy sauce, about 10 minutes. Taste, adjust the salt, and stir in two tablespoons of chopped cilantro if necessary.

Carefully place the prawns in the sauce in a single layer and cook for 2 minutes. Turn the prawns to cook the other sides and add the cod. (Discard any juices in the bowl.) The fish will be partly submerged. Cook until the fish is tender and just cooked through 2 to 3 minutes.

Remove from heat, drizzle in the remaining one tablespoon *of dendê oil, and sprinkle with the remaining two tablespoons of* chopped cilantro. Slice the remaining lime into wedges. Serve immediately with steamed rice and lime wedges for squeezing. served with rice and farofa.

Now, about those wines…

Argentinian Chardonnay – A Santa Ana or Mascota Vineyards are good bets.

Rose Reserva Concha y Toro – Excellent

Burgundy Pinot Noir – Louis Jadot is reasonably priced

Alsatian Pinot Blanc – Trimbach Pinot Blanc 2022

Osso Buco – Brazilian Style from Sao Paulo

Ingredients

Sauce

800 g veal or beef osso buco note that this weight includes bones; if substituting for boneless meat, this would be around 500g
1 tbsp flour

2+1 tbsp extra virgin olive oil. We used Rio Vista Olives' Nothin'
But Classic
half head of fennel chopped
One onion diced
One carrot diced
One head of garlic peeled and crushed lightly under the side of a
knife
handful of parsley stems chopped
2–3 large sprigs rosemary
small handful of sage leaves
1 tsp dried thyme
1 tsp fennel seeds
1 tsp black peppercorns
2 tbsp tomato paste
½ cup dry white wine
500 ml beef bone broth we used our frozen pressure cooker bone
broth, but you can substitute with any stock
2–3 bay leaves
salt to season

Gremolata
handful of parsley
zest of half a lemon
One small clove garlic
1 tbsp lemon juice

Instructions

Preheat the oven to 180 degrees Celsius.

Pat the osso buco dry with paper towels and dredge in the flour. Shake loose any excess.

Start the sauce off with a *soffrito*: put the fennel, onion, carrot, garlic, and all spices apart from the bay leaves into a cold enameled cast iron pot, with two tbsps of olive oil. Cook gently at low-medium heat, stirring regularly, until the fennel softens and the onion becomes transparent, about 15–20 minutes.

While cooking, heat 1 tbsp oil in a frying pan on high heat. Brown the meat on all sides and remove it from the pan. Note that if you can remove burnt flour from the pan, pour the remaining oil into the main pot containing your soffrito.

Stir the tomato paste into the soffritto and cook for 2–3 minutes before deglazing with the white wine.

Add the meat, bone broth, and bay leaves to the pot and season to taste.

Bring to a gentle boil, and then transfer to the oven.

Cook in the oven for two ½ to 3 hours or until the meat falls off the bone. Occasionally check the moisture levels and add water if it starts to get too dry.

Remove the bones and bay leaves. Scoop any bone marrow out of the bones and stir back through the sauce. Gently break the meat apart with a wooden spoon.

To make the gremolata, loosely blend or chop the parsley, lemon zest juice, and garlic. Serve on top of the osso buco.

Now, about those wines…

Barolo is a red wine produced in the Piedmont region of Italy. It is usually served with something other than cheeseburgers. This is a fine, highly reputable wine. The Nebbiolo grape is difficult to grow, and the wine requires a long aging process in oak barrels, which adds to the cost.

Châteauneuf-du-Pape, a fragrant cabernet-based wine that can pair well with osso buco (Never question the culinary wisdom or pairing insight of the Pope!)

Brunello di Montalcino is a Tuscan red wine considered by many to be "Italy's ultimate red."

If you are looking for a dark horse, I suggest a bold, ripe Petit Verdot. Its big flavors support equally big-flavored foods: aged or smoked hard cheeses, grilled steak, and roast duck.

BOLIVIAN *PINCANTE DE POLLO*

This is a trendy Bolivian dish from Cochabamba, a city in Bolivia's center. There are probably as many recipes for this spicy chicken dish as Bolivian cooks.

Ingredients

6 Chicken thighs
2 tsp Vegetable oil
One large Red bell pepper, cut into strips
3 White onions, chopped

2 Roma tomatoes, chopped

3 Garlic cloves, minced

3 Ajíes panca peppers

OR 5 oz. Ají panca paste

½ cup Green peas, cooked (firm)

Three cups Chicken broth

1 Chicken stock cube (or vegetable stock)

½ tsp Salt

½ tsp Pepper

½ tsp Cumin

½ tsp Oregano

$^6/_7$ Potatoes, small

Your choice of side (Chuño, long grain white rice, pasta) – optional

⅓ cup Breadcrumbs (optional)

Instructions

In a pot, boil water and leave potatoes in to cook, with the skin still on.

In a separate pot or Dutch oven, add ¼ cup oil and heat.

Fry chicken in the Dutch oven until golden.

Remove the Dutch oven from heat and set aside. Save the used oil.

Add the remaining ¼ cup oil to a saucepan and turn on low heat.

Sauté onions until translucent. Stir often.

Add the garlic, bell pepper, tomatoes, cumin, oregano, and ají panca peppers or paste. Sauté on low heat for 3–4 minutes until aromatic.

Add broth. Cover and simmer for 15 minutes.

Add the mixture from the saucepan into the Dutch oven, mixing with the chicken well.

Put the Dutch oven on low heat and season it with salt.

Cover and let simmer for 30 minutes.

Turn off the heat and add already-cooked peas.

Serve with cooked potatoes and long grain rice or your choice of side dish.

Now, about those wines…

Kohlberg Stelar *'Ugni" Blanc*, an excellent local wine, goes perfectly with a spicy dish. When in doubt, go local! It was a surprising winner.

A Pino Grigio or even a Chardonnay. All three play well with this dish.

ABOUT THE AUTHOR

Richard Rogers is a third-generation francophone who grew up in Paris during the 1950s and 1960s. His family's roots in France date back to 1912. His father was raised in the 16th arrondissement of Paris in the early 1930s, while his mother spent her summers in the South of France. In addition to France, Rogers' childhood was marked by time  spent in Belgium and the Democratic Republic of Congo, where his father served as a CIA officer.

Rogers' most recent book, *Whispers of the Americas*, takes readers on a culinary journey along well-traveled roads, offering a rich taste of diverse cultures, stories, and flavors. Divided into thoughtfully crafted sections, the book provides glimpses into the many places he has explored, focusing on the destinations and the people, connections, and shared experiences that shaped his travels. Each location he writes about reveals a distinct cuisine that plays a pivotal role in the narrative, underscoring the transformative power of food and travel in bringing people together and showing the shared beauty that unites us all.

His previous work, *Memories & Footprints: Adventures in Good Taste*, takes readers on a gastronomic adventure from Paris to the port city of Antwerp and onward to Brussels, offering a deep dive into the culture, people, and food of these historic cities. Having lived in France and Belgium, Rogers writes authentically about the places he knows well, interspersing his narrative with amusing tales of his father's cloak-and-dagger career as a CIA officer in Paris, the Congo, and Antwerp.

Rogers brings a similarly international perspective in his second book, *A Foreign Port of Entry*. This work explores the visual, cultural, and historical richness of cities such as Saigon, Mumbai, Istanbul, and Cairo. In this exciting adventure, he skillfully weaves travel, mystery, Cold War intrigue, and his experiences in the Congo. His storytelling is punctuated by humor and an appreciation for the exotic cuisines of these far-flung destinations, celebrating the transformative power of travel and the beauty of diverse cultures.

In his debut book, *A Long Look Back: A Sentimental Journey of an American Growing Up in France*, Rogers reflects on his boyhood in Paris and summers spent at his family's home in Brittany. These recollections, set against the region's rugged coastline and emerald-blue waters, provide a vivid, sentimental backdrop for his writing and serve as a wellspring of inspiration. It is an undeniably warm-hearted, tender journey into a France of yesteryear.

DID YOU ENJOY THIS BOOK? YOU CAN HELP ME!

As a relatively new author, having published three books, your support means the world to me. If you enjoyed this book (and I hope you did!), I would be incredibly grateful if you could take a moment to leave a review. Reader feedback is invaluable and helps others discover new stories they might love. Whether you bought the paperback or the e-book, leaving a review on Amazon is quick and easy. Your words have the power to make a big difference— thank you for considering it!

I appreciate any help you can provide.

Richard H Rogers
amazon/author/richard-h-rogers

February 2024
Available on Amazon

Memories & Footprints: Adventures in Good Taste takes readers on a rich culinary journey along a well-traveled road. The author leads you from the enchanting streets of Paris to the often-overlooked port city of Antwerp—steeped in centuries of history and renowned as a vibrant hub for the global diamond trade. From there, the adventure continues to Brussels, Belgium's grand capital. Drawing from personal experiences living in both countries, the author writes with authenticity and deep affection for the cultures, people, and cuisine. With a seamless blend of culinary insights, cultural reflections, regional history, and exquisite dining experiences—from elegant meals to homey bistro fare—this book is a heartfelt exploration of food and travel.

with rich descriptions of places, sometimes marked by sobering realities, while each destination showcases a distinct cuisine that plays a pivotal role in the adventure. Through the lens of food and travel, the author highlights the transformative power of these experiences and the shared beauty that connects people across the globe.

An engaging exotic travelogue: "This book provides a feel for what traveling to exotic and sometimes volatile destinations would feel like. The author describes the architecture, geography, political climate, and especially the food and people of each location in a way that allows the reader to experience the journey with him. I learned a lot and enjoyed the trips." SDF, December 2023.

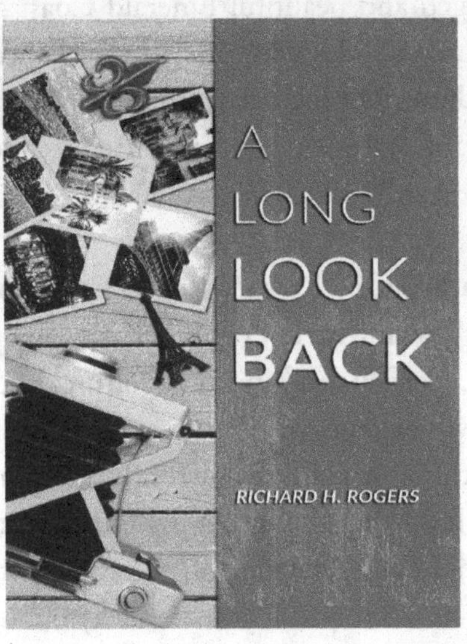

December 2023
Available on Amazon

The author writes with profound passion, drawing deeply from personal themes. He fondly recalls his boyhood days in Paris and the long, seemingly endless summers spent at the family's old house in Brittany. These memories are vividly set against the region's picturesque, rugged coastline and the striking emerald-blue waters. This vibrant landscape continues to serve as an endless source of inspiration and profound sentimentality for the author.

A warm-hearted, tender journey into a France of yesteryear: "This entertaining, often humorous, sentimental journey is set first in the rugged and beautiful Emerald Coast of Brittany and then in Paris. It concludes with unique travel and delicious food experiences as the author meanders from Lyon to the Côte d'Azur. It is an undeniably excellent, warm-hearted, tender journey into France of yesteryear." JRR 2023.

Growing up in France: "Richard Rogers has written a delightful tale of his years growing up in France and returning time and time again. Rogers covers France's history, culture, and cuisine in an easy read that will be enjoyed whether you are intimately familiar with France or thinking about going for the first time. His detailed descriptions of food and dining throughout the various regions of France will undoubtedly inspire you to visit France or at least to seek out a French restaurant if you are lucky enough to have one near you. I understand Richard Rogers is working on a second book, which I am anxiously looking forward to." LW, 2023.

A Love of France and Food: "A Love of France and Food A Love of France and Food: "The author's love of France comes through in short stories of growing up as part of an ex-pat family. If you need a primer on food in various, it's here, plus some recipes full of tasty calories. is a book that you can sit down and read a little bit at a time to satisfy the Francophile in you." RT, April 2023.

Lovely Memoir of Childhood in France: "I greatly enjoyed reading this memoir of an American boy and his family growing up in France in the 1950s. evocation of his "happy place" in

Bretagne, where they owned a house and spent summers, was detailed and evocative. Best of all, the descriptions of the meals that Rogers remembers from his childhood. He even includes recipes! This book has inspired me to revisit France and sample the authentic cuisine he describes. For now, I must be content with our local Pain Quotidien croissants while listening to Edith Piaf." JC, December 2022.